GCSE OCR Gateway
Core Science
Foundation Workbook

This book is for anyone doing **GCSE OCR Gateway Core Science** at foundation level.
It covers everything you'll need for your year 10 exams.

It's full of **tricky questions**... each one designed to make you **sweat**
— because that's the only way you'll get any **better**.

There are questions to see **what facts** you know. There are questions
to see how well you can **apply those facts**. And there are questions
to see what you know about **how science works**.

It's also got some daft bits in to try and make the whole
experience at least vaguely entertaining for you.

What CGP is all about

Our sole aim here at CGP is to produce the highest
quality books — carefully written, immaculately presented
and dangerously close to being funny.

Then we work our socks off to get them
out to you — at the cheapest possible prices.

Contents

Published by CGP

Editors:
Katie Braid, Emma Elder, David Hickinson, Edmund Robinson, Helen Ronan, Lyn Setchell,
Hayley Thompson, Jane Towle, Dawn Wright.

Contributors:
Steve Coggins, Frederick Langridge, Andy Rankin, Claire Ruthven, Adrian Schmit,
Sidney Stringer Community School, Jim Wilson, Chris Workman.

ISBN: 978 1 84146 711 5

With thanks to Charlotte Burrows, Philip Dobson, Ian Francis, Helena Hayes and Julie Jackson
for the proofreading.

With thanks to Jan Greenway, Laura Jakubowski and Laura Stoney for the copyright research.

Groovy website: www.cgpbooks.co.uk

Printed by Elanders Ltd, Newcastle upon Tyne.
Jolly bits of clipart from CorelDRAW®
Based on the classic CGP style created by Richard Parsons.

Fitness and Blood Pressure

Q1   Circle the correct word in each pair to complete the sentences below.

a)   Blood pressure is at its **highest / lowest** when the heart contracts.
This is called the **diastolic / systolic** pressure.

b)   Blood pressure is at its **highest / lowest** when the heart relaxes.
This is called the **diastolic / systolic** pressure.

c)   Blood pressure is measured in **mmPb / mmHg**.

Q2   Draw lines to match up the boxes and complete the sentences.

Being fit...

means being free from disease.

Being healthy...

measures how well you can perform physical tasks.

Q3   **Blood** is **pumped** around the body under **pressure**.

a)   What causes the blood to be under pressure?

....

b)   Explain why it's important that the blood is under pressure.

....

Q4   Jack has **high blood pressure**. He is overweight, eats very few fruits and vegetables and relies mostly on ready meals and take-aways. He does no regular exercise.

Suggest two ways in which Jack might reduce his blood pressure without taking drugs.

1. ....

2. ....

2

Fitness and Blood Pressure

Q5 The table shows some information on the **lifestyles** of Tricia and Dave.

Name	Occupation	Cigarettes smoked per day	Units of alcohol drunk per week
Tricia	Retired	0	4
Dave	Stock broker	40	28

a) Look at the table. How many more units of alcohol does Dave drink each week compared to Tricia?

....

b) Based on the information in the table, who do you think is **more likely** to have **high blood pressure** — Tricia or Dave? Give **one** reason for your answer.

....

....

Q6 You can measure someone's **fitness** by measuring their **stamina**.

a) Suggest **one** way you could measure someone's stamina.

....

b) Stamina is a good indicator of **cardiovascular efficiency**.
What is cardiovascular efficiency? Tick the box next to the correct answer.

The ability of the heart to supply the muscles with oxygen. ☐

The ability of veins to return blood to the heart. ☐

How fast the lungs supply the blood with oxygen. ☐

How fast the heart pumps. ☐

c) Apart from stamina and cardiovascular efficiency, give three things that could be measured to assess fitness.

1. ....

2. ....

3. ....

Module B1 — Understanding Ourselves

High Blood Pressure and Heart Disease

Q1   Complete the following sentences by circling the correct word in each pair.

a) Eating too much salt can **increase / decrease** your blood pressure.

b) Having a diet high in salt can **increase / decrease** your risk of developing heart disease.

Q2   Use all of the words from the list to complete the paragraph below. Some of the words may be used more than once.

plaques	reduced	arteries	cholesterol	heart attack

A diet high in saturated fat has been linked to high levels of

.... in the blood. If you have too much

.... in your body, it can start to build up in

your .... This forms ....

in the artery walls, causing the arteries to narrow. The flow of blood is

...., which can lead to a ....

Q3   Amy smokes cigarettes regularly. She has **high blood pressure** and her doctor thinks that her **smoking** is causing it.

a) High blood pressure increases Amy's risk of developing which health problem? Circle the correct answer from the list below.

        heart disease   **liver disease**   **obesity**   **flu**

Nicotine and **carbon monoxide** are both found in cigarette smoke.

b) How does **nicotine** increase blood pressure? Tick the box next to the correct answer.

    1. By widening the arteries. ☐

    2. By decreasing heart rate, so the heart contracts less often. ☐

    3. By increasing heart rate, so the heart contracts more often. ☐

c) Explain how **carbon monoxide** can increase blood pressure.

....

....

....

Eating Healthily

Q1 Draw lines to join each **nutrient** to what it's made from.

Carbohydrate

Protein

Fat

Amino acids

Glycerol

Simple sugars

Fatty acids

Q2 **Protein** is an important part of a balanced diet.

a) i) Circle the group below which needs to eat a **high protein diet**.

Office workers

Teenagers

The elderly

ii) Why does this group need to eat a high protein diet?
Circle the correct answer below.

They're still growing.

They're old.

They have busy jobs.

b) Write a 'T' next to the statement below that is **true**.

> 1. The body never uses protein as an energy source. ....
>
> 2. The body only uses protein as an energy source in emergencies. ....
>
> 3. The body regularly uses protein as an energy source. ....

Q3 Some people do not include certain foods in their diet for **religious**, **personal** or **medical reasons**.

a) Which of the following is a **medical reason** for avoiding certain foods?
Underline the correct answer.

Having an allergy to certain foods.   **Not liking the taste of certain foods.**

b) Some people choose to be vegetarians. Suggest one **personal reason** they might have for this.

....

Eating Healthily

Q4 A **balanced diet** contains all the nutrients you need to stay healthy.

a) Complete the table to show the **main functions** of some of the nutrients in our diet.

Nutrient	Function
Carbohydrates	
	Growth and repair of tissues.
Fats	
Vitamin C	
	To make haemoglobin for healthy blood.

b) Give **one** reason why **fibre** is also needed as part of a balanced diet.

....

c) i) Name **one** substance **not mentioned** in parts **a)** or **b)**, which is also needed for a balanced diet.

....

ii) Why is this substance needed as part of a balanced diet?

....

Q5 Read each sentence below. In each case, say which person you would expect to need **more carbohydrate** in their diet each day and **explain** why.

a) Alice works as a gardener, while Emily works in an office.

....

b) Thandi goes to the gym every day. Her friend Helen watches TV instead.

....

c) James walks his dog every evening, while Michael plays computer games.

....

Top Tips: Eating a balanced diet is dead important — but not everyone needs to eat exactly the same stuff. For example, sporty people like football players need food with lots of carbohydrates to give them energy, whereas I need a constant supply of tea and chocolate. Yum.

Diet Problems

Q1   **Obesity** means being 20% (or more) over recommended body weight.

    a)   Underline any health problems in the list below that have been linked to obesity.

        heart disease   hepatitis   influenza   breast cancer   scurvy   diabetes

    b)   Name **one** other health problem linked to obesity.

        ....

Q2   **Kwashiorkor** is a condition caused by eating too little protein.

    a)   Give **two** reasons why this condition is common in developing countries.

        ....

        ....

    b)   Calculate the **EAR** (Estimated Average daily Allowance) of protein for a 75 kg man.
        Use the formula in the box below.

       | **EAR (in g) = 0.6 × body mass (in kg)** | ....

                                                          ....

Q3   **Anorexia** is an eating disorder that can lead to a **poor diet**.
       One possible cause of anorexia is **low self esteem**.

    a)   Suggest **one** other possible cause of this disorder.

        ....

    b)   Suggest **one** health problem that a poor diet might cause.

        ....

Q4   **Body mass index (BMI)** is calculated to help determine a person's ideal weight.

    a)   Daniel is 1.6 m tall and weighs 64 kg. Calculate his BMI.

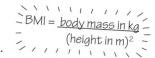

$$BMI = \frac{body\ mass\ in\ kg}{(height\ in\ m)^2}$$

        ....

    b)   Look at the table on the right.
       What is Daniel's weight description?

Body Mass Index	Weight Description
below 18.5	underweight
18.5 - 24.9	normal
25 - 29.9	overweight
30 - 40	moderately obese
above 40	severely obese

        ....

Infectious Disease

Q1 Tick the box next to the statement which is **true**.

1. All diseases can be passed on from person to person. ☐

2. Infectious diseases can be passed on from person to person. ☐

3. Non-infectious diseases can be passed on from person to person. ☐

4. Genetic diseases are a type of infectious disease. ☐

Q2 **Infectious** diseases are caused by **pathogens**.

a) What is a pathogen?

....

b) What are the symptoms of an infectious disease caused by?

....

c) Draw lines to match up the following diseases with the type of pathogen that causes them.

cholera   fungus

malaria   virus

flu   bacteria

athlete's foot   protozoa

Q3 **Circle** the correct words to complete the sentences below.

Malaria is a disease caused by a micro-organism called a **virus / protozoan**.

The micro-organism is a **parasite / guest** and the organism it infects is called

a **host / agent**. The disease is carried from person to person by mosquitoes.

An organism which transfers a disease without actually getting it is called

a **vector / insect**. Mosquitoes feed on **blood / snot**. When they bite an

old / infected animal they take in the malarial micro-organism and then pass

it on to the next animal they bite.

Top Tip: Infectious disorders can be spread by all sorts of means, including the air. That's why you should always cover your mouth when you sneeze — because if you don't, you're putting loads of lovely little germs into the air, ready for other people to breathe in. Nice.

8

Infectious Disease

Q4 The body has several ways of keeping out pathogens.

a) Name **three** parts of the body that help to keep out pathogens.

....

b) Below are examples of how some pathogens enter the body.
In each case, describe how the body can help to keep out the micro-organism.

i) Some bacteria can enter the body through cuts in the skin.

....

ii) Some viruses can enter your body when you breathe.

....

c) Some pathogens can enter the body in food and drink.

i) What part of the body defends against the entry of micro-organisms in food and drink?

....

ii) What does this part of the body produce to kill pathogens?

....

Q5 **TB** is an infectious disease spread through the air. The graph shows how the **incidence** of TB tends to change with the gross income of the population, worldwide.

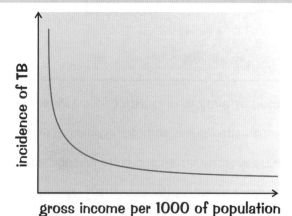

Gross income is a way of measuring how rich a country is — so the higher the gross income, the richer the country.

a) Describe how the incidence of TB changes as gross income increases.

....

b) Apart from income, suggest another factor that might affect
the incidence of disease in a particular country.

....

Module B1 — Understanding Ourselves

Preventing and Treating Infectious Disease

Q1   Circle the correct words to complete the paragraph.

> If you're infected with a **pathogen** / **antibiotic** for a second time, your **red blood cells** / **white blood cells** will recognise it and kill it so you don't become ill. This is immunity. In active immunity the immune system makes its own **antibodies** / **antigens**, but in passive immunity they come from **vaccination** / **another organism**.

Q2   **White blood cells** protect the body from infection.

   a) Give two ways that they do this.

      1. ....

      2. ....

   b) Fill in each of the gaps in the paragraph using the correct word from the list below.

antigens	antibodies	white	kill

> The .... blood cells recognise the .... on the surface of pathogens. They then make ...., which lock onto and .... the invading pathogens.

   c) Which of the following can stop you from getting certain diseases? Circle the correct answer.

      antibiotics   auxins   immunisation   antigens

Q3   Rachel has a virus, but when she visits her doctor he refuses to give her **antibiotics** to clear up her infection.

Think about the type of pathogens antibiotics are effective against.

   a) Explain why her doctor is right.

      ....

      ....

   b) Why type of drug could her doctor prescribe?

      ....

Cancer and Drug Development

Q1 New drugs have to be **tested** before they're used.

a) Give two reasons why new drugs have to be tested.

1. ....

2. ....

b) Write numbers in the boxes below to show the correct **order** in which drugs are tested.

☐ Drug is tested on human tissue

☐ Drug is tested on live animals

☐ Human volunteers are used to test the drug

☐ Drug is tested using computer models

c) Suggest a reason why some people are against testing drugs on animals.

....

d) Why are drugs tested using computer models? Tick the box next to the **two** correct answers.

Because it's illegal to test drugs on humans. ☐

To predict what a human's response will be to a drug. ☐

To identify what drugs might be useful. ☐

To see if the drug is poisonous. ☐

Q2 **Cancer** is caused by cells dividing out of control.

a) Give **one** example of a change that people can make to their **lifestyle**, which might reduce their risk of getting cancer.

....

b) Give **one** example of a change that people can make to their **diet**, which might reduce their risk of getting cancer.

....

Drugs: Use and Harm

Q1 a) What is a **drug**?

....

b) Tick the box to show whether the following statements are **true** or **false**.

True False

i) Drugs are never useful. ☐ ☐

ii) Tolerance is a physical need for a drug. ☐ ☐

iii) Rehabilitation is where a person gets help and support to stop using drugs. ☐ ☐

iv) Drugs which are available on prescription can be harmful if misused. ☐ ☐

c) Some people can become **addicted** to drugs. What does this mean?

....

....

Q2 **Complete** the table below, which shows different types of drug and their effects on the body.

Type of drug	Example	Effects
Depressants		
	Paracetamol	Block nerve impulses to reduce pain
Stimulants		Increase the activity of the brain
	Anabolic steroids	
		Distort what's seen and heard

Q3 Two people were arrested and charged with **drug offences**. Janice had been found taking a class C drug. Paul had been found taking a class A drug.

Who is likely to receive the **most severe** punishment? Explain your answer.

....

....

Smoking and Alcohol

Q1 Look at the following **health problems** and circle four that are linked with **smoking**.

| heart disease | bronchitis | lung cancer |

| liver disease | emphysema | poor memory |

Q2 There are serious long-term effects of drinking too much **alcohol**.

Name **two** organs that can be damaged by drinking too much alcohol.

....

Q3 In the UK, the legal limit for alcohol in the blood when driving is **80 mg per 100 cm³**. The table shows the number of 'units' of alcohol in different drinks.

DRINK	ALCOHOL UNITS
1 pint of strong lager	3
1 pint of beer	2
1 single measure of whisky	1

a) Bill drinks two pints of strong lager. How many units of alcohol has he had?

....

b) Give four effects that drinking alcohol might have on Bill that would make it **unsafe** for him to drive.

1. .... 2. ....

3. .... 4. ....

c) One **unit** increases the blood alcohol level by over **20 mg per 100 cm³** in most people.

i) Calculate the level of alcohol in Bill's blood in mg per 100 cm³.

....

....

You'll need your answer to part a) to do the calculation.

ii) Can Bill legally drive?

....

Smoking and Alcohol

Q4 Burning **cigarettes** release nicotine, tar, carbon monoxide and particulates.
Draw lines to match each product to its **effect(s)**. One's already been done for you.

Makes smoking addictive.

Carbon monoxide

Contains carcinogens.

Builds up in lung tissue (causing irritation).

Nicotine

Tar

Causes irritation by covering cilia in the airways.

Stops the blood carrying as much oxygen.

Particulates

Q5 The graph below shows how the number of **smokers** aged between 35 and 54 in the UK has changed since 1950.

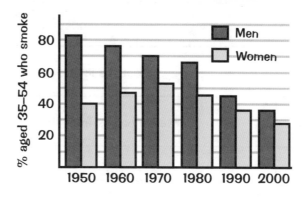

a) What percentage of **men** smoked in 1970?

....

b) Describe what happened to the number of **female smokers** between 1950 and 2000.

....

....

c) Explain how smoking causes **smoker's cough.**

....

....

....

Top Tips: The facts about what cigarettes and alcohol do to your body are pretty nasty and off-putting. It's good for you to know them, so you can choose a healthy lifestyle.

The Eye

Q1   Write **labels** in the spaces to complete the diagram of a human eye.

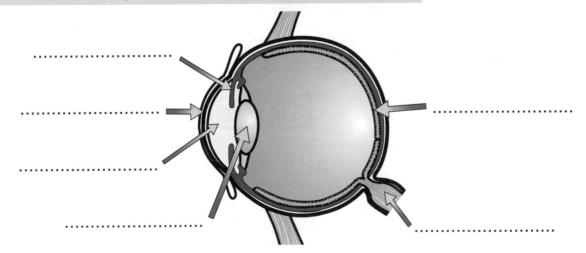

....

....

....

....

Q2   **Complete the table** about the functions of different parts of the eye.

Part of the eye	Function
....	Focuses light on the retina
....	Carries impulses from the eye to the brain
Retina	....
Cornea	....
....	Controls how much light enters the pupil

Q3   Complete the following diagram by drawing the **path of light** through the eye to the retina. Label where the light is **refracted** into the eye.

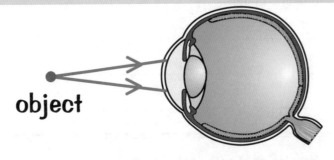

object

Vision

Q1 **Short-sighted people** are unable to focus on distant objects.

a) Which of the following could cause short-sightedness? Underline the **two** correct answers.

the eyeball being too long

the lens being the wrong shape

damage to the retina

squinting too much

b) Explain how short-sightedness is caused by the answers you chose in part **a)**.

....

....

Q2 The pictures below show two birds, each with a different type of **vision**.

Binocular vision

Monocular vision

a) i) **Binocular** vision allows the bird to judge distances well.
Explain how binocular vision works.

....

....

ii) Give **one** disadvantage of **binocular** vision.

....

b) Birds with **monocular vision** can't judge distances very easily.
What **advantage** does monocular vision give them?

....

Neurones and Reflexes

Q1   Circle the correct answer to complete each of the following sentences.

a)   Reflexes happen **quickly** / **slowly**.

b)   The main purpose of a reflex is to **protect** / **display** the body.

c)   Reflexes happen **with** / **without** you thinking about them.

d)   The pathway taken by a reflex is called a **reflex arc** / **reflex curve**.

e)   Voluntary responses are under the **unconscious** / **conscious** control of the brain.

Q2   **Neurones** carry information around the body.

a)   Label the diagram below showing a typical **motor neurone**.

b)   What part of the motor neurone does the **nerve impulse** pass along?

....

Q3   Place numbers in the boxes to show the **passage of a reflex**.
The first one's been done for you.

☐ Response   ☐ Sensory neurone   ☐ Effector   ☐ Relay neurone

☐ Motor neurone   [1] Stimulus   ☐ Receptor

Q4   Some parts of the body are known as the **CNS**.

a)   What do the letters **CNS** stand for?   ....

b)   Look at the diagram on the right.

  i) Which letter is pointing to part of the CNS? ....

  ii) Which letter is pointing to part of the peripheral nervous system? ....

c)   Name the two main parts of the CNS.

  1. ....

  2. ....

Module B1 — Understanding Ourselves

Homeostasis

Q1 Put ticks in the boxes to show whether each technique helps to **warm up** or **cool down** the body.

	Warm up	Cool down
a) Shivering.	☐	☐
b) Increasing the blood flow near the surface of the skin.	☐	☐
c) Exercising.	☐	☐
d) Putting on more clothes.	☐	☐

Q2 a) What does the word **homeostasis** mean?

....

b) Name three things that need to be kept at the right level in the body.

1. ....

2. ....

3. ....

Q3 The human body is usually maintained at a **constant temperature**.

a) What temperature is the human body usually kept at? ....

b) Circle any of the places below that are commonly used to **measure body temperature**.

nose   mouth   ear   belly button   finger   hair   anus

c) Give two methods of measuring body temperature.

1. ....

2. ....

d) Name **one** condition you can get if you're exposed to:

i) **high** temperatures for a long time. ....

ii) **low** temperatures for a long time. ....

Q4 Explain how **sweating** helps to lower your body temperature.

....

....

Controlling Blood Sugar

Q1 a) Name the **main hormone** involved in controlling blood sugar level.

....

b) i) Give the name of the **organ** that produces this hormone.

....

ii) Circle the **position** of this organ on the diagram on the right.

Q2 Use all of the words below to fill in the gaps in this passage about the control of diabetes.

pancreas   insulin   *two*   diet   sugary foods   rise

There are .... types of diabetes. Type 1 diabetes is where

the .... can't produce insulin. Type 2 diabetes is where

a person can't respond to insulin. In both cases the blood sugar level may

.... to dangerous levels. People with type 2 diabetes can

usually manage their disease by controlling their ....,

particularly by avoiding .... However, people with

type 1 diabetes also have to inject .... at mealtimes.

Q3 Blood sugar level is controlled by **hormones**.
Explain why nervous messages are faster than hormonal ones.

....

....

....

Top Tips: Although diabetes is a serious disease, many diabetics are able to control their blood sugar levels. They're able to carry on with normal lives and do most of the things they want. Sir Steve Redgrave even won a gold medal at the Olympics after he had been diagnosed with diabetes.

Plant Hormones and Growth

Q1 Tick the correct box to show whether the following statements are **true** or **false**.

True False

a) Plant shoots grow away from light. ☐ ☐

b) The response of plants to light is called phototropism. ☐ ☐

c) Plant roots grow towards light. ☐ ☐

d) Plant roots grow in the same direction that gravity acts. ☐ ☐

e) The roots of plants are positively geotropic. ☐ ☐

f) Growth towards light decreases a plant's chances of survival. ☐ ☐

Q2 The growth of plants is controlled by plant growth **hormones**.

a) **Fruit ripening** is an example of plant growth controlled by hormones.
Give **three** other examples of plant growth controlled in this way.

....

....

b) i) Name the group of **hormones** involved in the responses of plants to both **light** and **gravity**.

....

ii) How do plant hormones move through the plant? Circle the correct answer below.

by blood   **in solution**   **as electrical impulses**

Q3 Suzanne is doing an **experiment** to investigate the response of plant **shoots** to **light**. The equipment she uses is shown below on the left.

a) Draw how Suzanne could set up her equipment for this experiment in the box below.

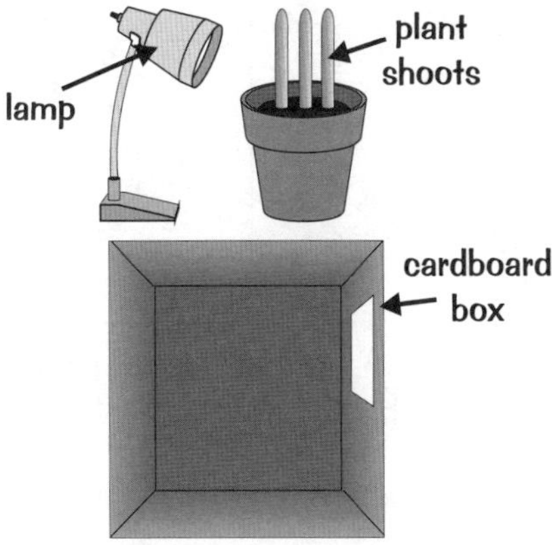

lamp
plant shoots
cardboard box

b) Describe what will happen to the plant shoots during this experiment.

....

Commercial Use of Plant Hormones

Q1   Describe four ways in which **plant hormones** can be used **commercially**.

1. ....

2. ....

3. ....

4. ....

Q2   Charlie sprayed a batch of **dormant** barley seeds with a dilute solution of a plant hormone. This caused all the seeds to germinate.

a)   Circle the correct word from each pair to complete the sentences below.

> **i)**   Germination is where a seed begins to **spread infections / grow**.
>
> **ii)**   The period when seeds won't germinate until they've been through certain conditions is called **dormancy / hibernation**.

b)   Suggest one reason why it's useful to be able to **control dormancy in plants**.

....

....

Q3   Sanjay grows barley in two neighbouring fields — **Field A** and **Field B**. The fields are an identical size, have the same soil and he uses the same fertilisers for both. The only difference is that he applies a **selective weedkiller** containing plant growth hormones to Field B but not Field A.

The graph shows the yield (amount of crop produced) for both fields over five years.

a)   What effect did the weedkiller have on crop yield?

....

....

b)   Did the plant growth hormones in the weedkiller affect the growth of the weeds, the crops or both? Explain your answer.

....

....

Commercial Use of Plant Hormones

Q4 Barry is investigating the effect of a **plant growth hormone** on the **growth of the roots** in some identical plant cuttings. His measurements are shown in the table.

a) Complete the table by calculating the increase in root length at each concentration.

Concentration of growth hormone (parts per million)	0	0.001	0.01	0.1	1
Length of root at start of investigation (mm)	20	20	20	20	20
Length of root 1 week after investigation started (mm)	26	32	28	23	21
Increase of root length (mm)					

b) On the grid below, plot a bar chart of the increase in root length against the concentration of plant growth hormone.

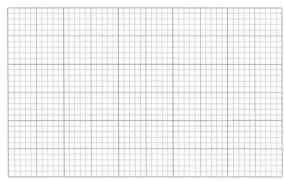

c) Which concentration of growth hormone caused the biggest increase in plant growth?

....

Q5 Ronald owns a fruit farm on which he grows satsumas.
The fruit is picked **before it is ripe** and then transported to market.

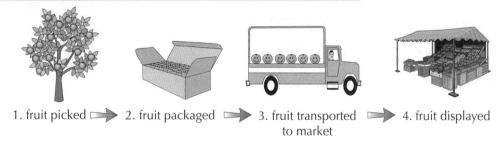

1. fruit picked ⇒ 2. fruit packaged ⇒ 3. fruit transported to market ⇒ 4. fruit displayed

a) How could the unripened satsumas be ripened in time to reach the market?

....

b) At what stage in the diagram above should the satsumas be ripened?

....

Genes and Chromosomes

Q1 Complete the passage by choosing from the words given below.

DNA	nucleus	genes	characteristics

Chromosomes are long lengths of ....

They're found in the ....

Chromosomes carry ...., which control

the development of different ....

Q2 Write out these structures in order of size, **starting with the smallest.**

nucleus   gene

chromosome   cell

....

Q3 a) Tick the correct boxes to show whether each statement is **true** or **false**.

True False

i) Human body cells contain 46 chromosomes. ☐ ☐

ii) In most body cells, chromosomes come in matching pairs. ☐ ☐

iii) All species have the same number of chromosomes. ☐ ☐

b) Write a corrected version of each false statement in the space below.

....

....

Top Tips: Ah, genes and chromosomes — the Ant and Dec of the genetic world. Make sure you know what they are — it might just pick you up some lovely marks in the exam.

Genes and the Environment

Q1   What are '**alleles**'? Underline the correct answer below.

'Alleles' are all the genes found on a pair of chromosomes.

'Alleles' are different versions of the same gene.

'Alleles' are genetically identical organisms.

Q2   Give the **dominant** and **recessive** characteristics from the descriptions below.

a)   Two flies, one with red eyes and one with white eyes, fall in love and get it on.
All their offspring have red eyes.

dominant characteristic: ....   **recessive characteristic:** ....

b)   Rats with white hair were bred with rats with black hair. The majority of the offspring are black.

dominant characteristic: ....   **recessive characteristic:** ....

c)   Tall pea plants were bred with dwarf pea plants. All the offspring were tall.

dominant characteristic: ....   **recessive characteristic:** ....

Q3   Jenny thinks that her **intelligence** is determined only by her **genes**.
Is she right? Explain your answer.

....

Q4   The **table** below gives the **heights** (to the nearest cm) of pupils in Year 7 at a school.

HEIGHT RANGE (cm)	NO. OF PUPILS
135–139	2
140–144	16
145–149	26
150–154	15
155–159	4
160–164	1

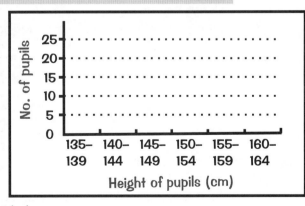

a)   Plot a bar chart for the results on the grid provided.

b)   Within which of the height ranges are the most students found? ....

c)   Underline the reason for the variation in the children's height.

genes only   environment only   both genes and environment

Causes of Genetic Variation

Q1   Genetic variation can be caused by **mutations**.
Tick the box next to the correct definition of a mutation.

    1.   A change in cell structure.   ☐

    2.   When two gametes join together.   ☐

    3.   A change to a gene.   ☐

    4.   When a body cell splits to form gametes.   ☐

Q2   The diagram below shows human **sperm** and **egg** cells combining to make a **fertilised** egg cell.
Write numbers on the nuclei of each cell to show how many **chromosomes** each contains.

egg   +   sperm   →   fertilised egg

Q3   **Circle** the correct word(s) in each pair to complete the sentences below.

a)   Sperm and egg cells are called **gametes** / **ovaries**.

b)   The body cells that sperm and egg cells are made from contain **23** / **46** chromosomes.

c)   A gamete contains chromosomes from **one parent** / **both parents**.

d)   Sperm and egg cells contain **the same** / **a different** number of chromosomes.

Q4   Fertilisation and the formation of gametes both cause **genetic variation**.

a)   How does the formation of gametes lead to genetic variation?

....

....

b)   **i)**   What is fertilisation?

....

    ii)   How does fertilisation lead to genetic variation?

....

....

Genetic Disorders and Sex Inheritance

Q1   **Genetic disorders** are inherited conditions.

a)   What are genetic disorders caused by? Circle the correct answer.

antigens   faulty genes   viruses   homeostasis   auxins

b)   i) Name **three** genetic disorders.

....

....

ii) Describe **one** of the genetic disorders you named in part **i**).

....

....

Q2   Use the words and letters below to fill in the gaps in this passage.

mammals		plants		
X	XX	XY	YY	Y

You don't need all the words in the list.

Everybody has two chromosomes that determine whether they are

male or female. These are the sex chromosomes.

The .... chromosome is present in both men and

women, but the .... chromosome is only present

in men. All women have the .... combination

of chromosomes. All men have the ....

combination of chromosomes. These chromosomes determine the

sex of all ....

My son Jeremy shall inherit my stamp collection and my chromosomes.

Q3   Describe an issue that might be raised by knowing that there's a **genetic disorder** in your **family**.

....

....

Top Tip: Lots of genetic disorders are pretty nasty, but thankfully research is being done to find ways of treating them. You don't need to know about treatments for the exam, but there are three examples of disorders you do need to learn — so make sure you've got them fixed in your head.

Mixed Questions — Module B1

Q1 Tick the box to show whether the following statements are **true** or **false**.

True False

a) All of your characteristics are controlled by your genes. ☐ ☐

b) There are dominant and recessive versions of characteristics like eye colour. ☐ ☐

c) Human gametes contain 23 pairs of chromosomes. ☐ ☐

d) Your body mass is controlled by both your genes and your environment. ☐ ☐

e) All men have two Y chromosomes. ☐ ☐

Q2 **Protein** is one of six nutrients needed for a **balanced diet**.

a) What are proteins made from? Circle the correct answer from the choice of words below.

amino acids   glycerol   fatty acids

b) What condition is likely to develop in people whose diets don't have enough protein?

....

c) Name three other substances needed for a balanced diet.

1. ....

2. ....

3. ....

d) A balanced diet can vary depending on someone's **religion**.
Give an example of religion affecting diet.

....

....

Q3 **Circle** the correct words from each pair to complete the paragraph below.

When you're too cold you produce **very little sweat / a lot of sweat**.

The blood flow to the surface of your skin is **increased / reduced**.

Smoking / shivering produces body heat through **respiration / burning**.

You can also **sweat more / add extra clothing** to help you stay warm.

Mixed Questions — Module B1

Q4 **Cocaine** and **nicotine** are both stimulant drugs. Cocaine is a Class A drug. Nicotine is legal and found in cigarettes.

a) Tick the box next to the name of the drug that could give the user a prison sentence.

COCAINE ☐   NICOTINE ☐

b) What effect do stimulants have on the brain?

....

c) What effect does nicotine have on blood pressure?

....

Q5 On the right is a diagram of the **human eye**.

a) Complete the diagram by labelling the **blind spot**.

b) i) Name the parts of the eye that **refract light**.

....

....

optic nerve

ii) Name the part of the eye that **contains light receptors**.

....

c) Which of the following is a condition caused by a lack of specialised cells in the retina? Circle the correct answer.

short-sightedness   red-green colour blindness   sickle cell anaemia

d) How do nervous impulses travel along the optic nerve? Circle the correct answer below.

as chemical impulses   as light   as electrical impulses

e) i) What causes **long-sightedness**?

....

ii) How does long-sightedness affect where images are brought into focus in the eye?

....

28

Mixed Questions — Module B1

Q6 Barney falls ill and develops a **temperature**. He thinks he has flu.

a) What could Barney use to measure his temperature?

....

b) Name the **type** of pathogen that causes the flu.

....

c) Write numbers in the boxes to show the correct order of events
when a pathogen enters the body.

☐ The white blood cells make antibodies.

☐ White blood cells travelling around the body come
across the antigens on the pathogen's surface.

☐ A pathogen gets into the body.

☐ Antibodies lock onto and kill the invading pathogen.

Q7 **Phototropism** and **geotropism** are the responses of plants to light and gravity.

a) Draw lines between the boxes to complete the sentences. One's already been done for you.

Positive phototropism is when...	plant shoots grow towards the light.
Negative phototropism is when...	plant roots grow in the direction of gravity.
Positive geotropism is when...	plant shoots grow away from gravity.
Negative geotropism is when...	plant roots grow away from light.

b) Fill in the missing word to complete the sentence below:

The group of plant hormones responsible for phototropism
and geotropism are called ....

Module B1 — Understanding Ourselves

Atoms, Molecules and Compounds

Q1 Say whether each of the sentences below is about the **nucleus** or the **electrons** of an atom.

a) Has a negative charge. ....

b) Found at the centre of an atom. ....

c) Can be lost from atoms. ....

d) Can be gained by atoms. ....

Q2 Chemical **formulas** can tell you what type of substance something is.

a) Circle the formula on the right that shows an **ion**.   C O_2 Na^+ H_2

b) Circle the formula on the right that shows a **molecule**.   H H_2O Ca^{2+} Cl^-

c) Circle the formula on the right that shows an **atom**. Cl^- CO_2 C H_2O

d) Circle the formula on the right that shows an **element**. O_2 H_2O CO_2 CH_4

e) Circle the formula on the right that shows a **compound**. H_2 H_2O O_2 Ca^{2+}

Q3 The sentences below all contain **one** mistake. Write a **correct** version of each sentence.

a) Negative ions are made when atoms lose electrons.

....

b) Positive ions are formed when atoms gain an electron.

....

c) Atoms can be held together by ionic or complimentary bonds.

....

Q4 **True** or **false**?

	True	False
a) In ionic bonding, ions share electrons.	☐	☐
b) Ions with opposite charges attract each other.	☐	☐
c) Elements that lose electrons form positive ions.	☐	☐
d) Covalent bonding is when atoms share electrons.	☐	☐

Chemical Formulas

Q1   The **displayed** formula for **ethanol** is shown on the right.

H—C—C—O—H (displayed formula with H H on top and H H on bottom)

a)   What is the **molecular** formula of ethanol?   ....

b)   How many **carbon** atoms does a molecule of ethanol contain?

....

c)   How many atoms does a molecule of ethanol contain **in total**?

....

Q2   **Chemical formulas** are used to show elements and compounds.

a)   Write the molecular formulas of the elements and compounds listed below.

   i) oxygen gas ....   **ii)** carbon dioxide   ....

   iii) water   ....   **iv)** carbon monoxide   ....

b)   State how many **oxygen** atoms there are in the compounds below.

   i) H_2SO_4 ....   **ii)** CH_3COOH ....

Q3   This is the molecular formula of **butane**.

$$CH_3(CH_2)_2CH_3$$

a)   State the total number of atoms in butane.

....

b)   In a molecule of butane, what is the total number of atoms of:

   i) carbon? ....   **ii)** hydrogen? ....

Q4   Complete the table to show the **molecular formulas** of methane, ethane and propane.

NAME	DISPLAYED FORMULA	MOLECULAR FORMULA
METHANE	H—C—H (with H on top and H on bottom)	a)
ETHANE	H—C—C—H (with H H on top and H H on bottom)	b)
PROPANE	H—C—C—C—H (with H H H on top and H H H on bottom)	c)

Chemical Equations

Q1   Complete the table below to show the **reactants** and the **products** in each of the equations.

Equation	Reactants	Products
$C + O_2 \rightarrow CO_2$		
nitrogen + hydrogen $\rightarrow$ ammonia		
$2Na + Cl_2 \rightarrow 2NaCl$		

Q2   This is the **equation** for burning hydrogen in air:

$$2H_2 + O_2 \rightarrow 2H_2O$$

a)   How many H and O atoms are shown on the **left-hand** side of the equation?

H ....   O ....

b)   How many H and O atoms are shown on the **right-hand** side of the equation?

H ....   O ....

c)   Is this equation balanced? Explain your answer.

....

Q3   Tick the correct box to show which of the following equations are **balanced** correctly.

		Correctly balanced	Incorrectly balanced
a)	$H_2 + Cl_2 \rightarrow 2HCl$	☐	☐
b)	$CuO + HCl \rightarrow CuCl_2 + H_2O$	☐	☐
c)	$N_2 + H_2 \rightarrow NH_3$	☐	☐
d)	$CuO + H_2 \rightarrow Cu + H_2O$	☐	☐
e)	$CaCO_3 \rightarrow CaO + CO_2$	☐	☐

$Fe_2O_3 + 3CO \rightarrow 2Fe + 3CO_2$

Top Tip: To find out if an equation is balanced or not, just take one type of atom at a time. Count them up on both sides, see if they match, then move on to the next type of atom. Easy as pie.

Chemical Equations

Q4 Here is the equation for how carbon **monoxide** is produced. It is **not** balanced correctly.

$$C + O_2 \rightarrow CO$$

Circle the **correctly balanced** version of this equation.

$$C + O_2 \rightarrow CO_2$$

$$C + O_2 \rightarrow 2CO$$

$$2C + O_2 \rightarrow 2CO$$

Q5 In a chemical reaction, **reactants** are changed into **products**.

a) **Magnesium** (Mg) can be burnt in **oxygen** (O_2) to form **magnesium oxide** (MgO).

i) What are the reactants and the products in this reaction?

Reactants: .... Products: ....

ii) Write the **word** equation for this reaction.

....

iii) Write the balanced **symbol** equation for the reaction.

....

b) **Methane** (CH_4) can be burnt in **oxygen** (O_2) to form **carbon dioxide** (CO_2) and **water** (H_2O).

i) What are the reactants and the products in this reaction?

Reactants: .... Products: ....

ii) Write the **word** equation for this reaction.

....

iii) Write the balanced **symbol** equation for the reaction.

Don't forget — the oxygen ends up in both products.

....

Q6 **Balance** the following symbol equations by writing numbers in the spaces.

a) CO_2 + ... H_2 $\rightarrow$ CH_4 + ... H_2O

b) K_2O + H_2O $\rightarrow$ .... KOH

c) $MgCO_3$ + ... HCl $\rightarrow$ $MgCl_2$ + H_2O + CO_2

d) .... Li + ... H_2O $\rightarrow$ .... LiOH + H_2

Food Additives

Q1   Draw lines to match up each type of **food additive** with its **use**.

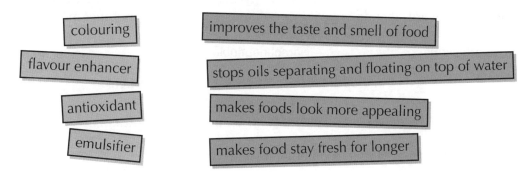

colouring

flavour enhancer

antioxidant

emulsifier

improves the taste and smell of food

stops oils separating and floating on top of water

makes foods look more appealing

makes food stay fresh for longer

Q2   Sue looks at the labels on some food packets to see what additives they have in them. She searches the internet to find out what each additive does.

This is what she finds:

ITEM	ADDITIVE	TYPE OF ADDITIVE
sausages	sodium ascorbate	antioxidant
cola	caramel	colouring
soup	monosodium glutamate	flavour enhancer
toothpaste	titanium dioxide	colouring

Use the information in the table to answer the questions below.

a)   Why is there sodium ascorbate in the sausages? Circle the correct answer.

To change the way the product looks.   To help stop the product going off as quickly.   To bring out the flavours of the food.

b)   Why is there caramel in the cola? Circle the correct answer.

To change the way the product looks.   To help stop the product going off as quickly.   To bring out the flavours of the food.

c)   Why is there monosodium glutamate in the soup? Circle the correct answer.

To change the way the product looks.   To help stop the product going off as quickly.   To bring out the flavours of the food.

d)   Why is there titanium dioxide in the toothpaste? Circle the correct answer.

To change the way the product looks.   To help stop the product going off as quickly.   To bring out the flavours of the food.

Q3   Antioxidants are used to help stop foods '**going off**' as quickly.

a)   Which element in the air makes food 'go off'? ....

b)   Name **two** foods that have antioxidants added to them.

....

Food Additives

Q4   **Emulsifiers** are added to chocolate drinks to stop the oils separating from the water.

a)   Circle the **two words** that describe the two different parts of an emulsifier molecule.

hydrochloric   arachnophobic   hydrophilic

hydrophobic   hydroponic

b)   i) Which part of the molecule is water loving?   ....

ii) Which part of the molecule is oil or fat loving?   ....

c)   Name a food that often contains an emulsifier.

....

Q5   Imran is investigating the effects of different food additives on a mixture of **olive oil** and **water**.

He sets up **four flasks** containing the same amounts of oil and water.
He adds **nothing** else to the first one, and either **additive A**, **B** or **C** to the others.
After five days he records their appearance and how they smell.

Additive used	After 5 days	
	Appearance	Smell
None	Oil floating on water	Unpleasant smell
A	Oil floating on water	No smell
B	Oil floating on water	Unpleasant smell
C	Oil and water mixed	Unpleasant smell

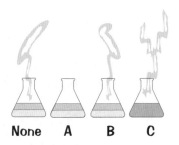

None   A   B   C

a)   Explain why the oil and water separate into two layers.

....

b)   Which one of the additives is:

i) An antioxidant? ....

ii) An emulsifier? ....

Think about what antioxidants and emulsifiers do and what effect they would have on the oil and water.

c)   Explain your answers to part **b)**.

i) ....

ii) ....

d)   Why does Imran set up a flask with **no additives** added?

....

Cooking and Chemical Change

Q1   Tick the box to show if the following statements are **true** or **false**.

		True	False
a)	Cooking is a reversible process.	☐	☐
b)	A chemical reaction has taken place if new substances are made.	☐	☐
c)	Cooking isn't a chemical reaction because it doesn't need any energy.	☐	☐

Q2   Complete the following passage by circling the correct words.

> Eggs and meat **contain** / **don't contain** protein.
>
> Protein molecules change **shape** / **atoms** when they are heated.
>
> This is called **destroying** / **denaturing**.
>
> The change is **reversible** / **irreversible**.

Q3   **Baking powder** contains **sodium hydrogencarbonate**, which breaks down when heated.

a)   Complete the following word equation.

sodium hydrogencarbonate →

.... **+ carbon dioxide +** ....

b)   Complete the symbol equation for the reaction above. Make sure it's **balanced**.

.... $NaHCO_3 \rightarrow Na_2CO_3 + CO_2 +$ ....

c)   What is this type of chemical reaction called? Circle the correct answer.

> neutralisation   combustion   thermal decomposition   respiration

d)   The chemical test for carbon dioxide is shown on the right.

   i) Name the solution marked 'A' in the diagram.

   ....

   ii) What would you expect to see if carbon dioxide was present?

   ....

e)   Explain why baking powder is used in cakes.

....

Perfumes

Q1 **Perfumes** are a type of cosmetic that smell nice.

Circle the **two** properties shown below that are useful in perfumes.

evaporates easily   very reactive

insoluble in water

viscous   toxic

Q2 a) Tick the boxes to show whether each of the following statements is **true** or **false**.

True False

i) Esters are commonly used as perfumes. ☐ ☐

ii) Alcohols react with acids to make esters. ☐ ☐

iii) Testing cosmetics on animals is banned in the EU. ☐ ☐

b) The sentences below both contain a mistake. Write out correct versions of the sentences.

i) Cosmetics can only be made from artificial sources.

....

ii) Esters cannot be made synthetically.

....

Q3 Fruity smelling **esters** can be made in the lab.

a) Complete the word equation for the **general** reaction used to make an ester.

                                                    acid catalyst
.... + ... $\xrightarrow{\hspace{2cm}}$ ester + water

b) Write the numbers 1-5 in the boxes to put the instructions into the right order for making an ester. The first one has been done for you.

☐	Warm the flask gently on an electric heating plate for 5 minutes.
1	Put 15 cm³ of ethanoic acid into a conical flask.
☐	When the flask has cooled down, pour its contents into a beaker containing sodium carbonate solution.
☐	Add 15 cm³ of ethanol and a few drops of an acid catalyst.
☐	Turn off the heat.

<u>*Perfumes*</u>

Q4 Some countries allow new perfumes to be tested on **animals**.

a) Explain why perfumes need to be tested before they are sold in the shops.

....

b) Give one **advantage** of testing cosmetic products on animals.

....

c) Give one **disadvantage** of testing cosmetic products on animals.

....

Q5 An **aftershave company** is making some new scents. The new compounds are **tested** to see if they are suitable to be used in aftershaves. The results of the tests are shown in the table.

Liquid	Does it evaporate easily?	Does it dissolve in water?	Does it react with water?
A	yes	no	yes
B	yes	yes	no
C	yes	no	no
D	no	no	no

a) Explain why it is important that the aftershave **evaporates** easily.

....

....

b) Would you want an aftershave to **dissolve in water**? Explain your answer.

....

c) Would you want an aftershave to **react with water**? Explain your answer.

....

d) Which one of the liquids A-D would you use as the scent in an aftershave? ....

e) Suggest a further test that should be carried out before the chemical is used in the aftershave.

....

> ## *Top Tip:* You've probably heard it a million times before, but if you're asked about something which you feel passionate about, like animal testing, you've got to give both points of view.

Solutions

Q1 Tick the correct boxes to show whether the following statements are **true** or **false**.

		True	False
a)	A solute is made by dissolving a solid in a liquid.	☐	☐
b)	A solvent is the liquid that the solid is dissolving into.	☐	☐
c)	A solution is a mixture of a solute and a solvent that doesn't separate out.	☐	☐
d)	A substance that will dissolve in a solvent is described as insoluble.	☐	☐
e)	Lots of esters make good solvents.	☐	☐
f)	Nail varnish remover dissolves nail varnish colours.	☐	☐
g)	If something is soluble it won't dissolve.	☐	☐

Q2 Read each of the following sentences and then list the **solute**, **solvent** and **solution** mentioned.

a) **Salt dissolves in water to form brine.**

Solute .... Solvent .... Solution ....

b) **A tincture can be made by dissolving iodine in alcohol.**

Solute .... Solvent .... Solution ....

c) **Gold is soluble in mercury and this mixture is an amalgam.**

Solute .... Solvent .... Solution ....

Q3 Neena is investigating the **solubility** of sodium chloride (salt) in different solvents.

She adds **10 g** of salt to **10 cm³** of each solvent and stirs it until no more salt will dissolve.
She filters each solution to remove any salt that didn't dissolve and lets it dry.
She then weighs the leftover salt. Her results are recorded in the table.

a) Complete the table by calculating the mass of salt that dissolved in each solvent.
The first one is done for you.

Solvent	Mass of salt that won't dissolve (g)	Mass of salt that dissolved (g)
water	6.8	3.2
methanol	9.8	
formic acid	9.5	
formamide	9.0	

Hint: mass of the salt dissolved = total mass of salt − mass of salt that won't dissolve.

b) Which is the best solvent in the table to use to dissolve salt?

....

__Paints and Pigments__

Q1   Explain why paint would be used on the objects below:

   a)   A bridge.

   ....

   b)   A bedroom wall.

   ....

Q2   Match each term on the left with the correct meaning on the right.

   pigment

   solvent

   binding medium

   sticks the pigment to the surface

   thins the paint

   gives paint its colour

Q3   Choose from the words below to complete the passage.

liquid	pigment	colloid	dissolved

   Paint is a .... — this is a kind of mixture.

   In a paint, particles of .... are dispersed in a ....

   The particles are not ....

Q4   Which of these diagrams correctly shows an **oil-based** paint? Circle the correct diagram.

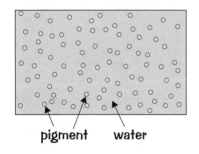

pigment   water

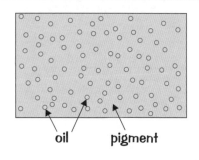

oil   pigment

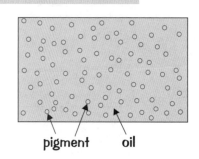

pigment   oil

Q5   Circle the correct words to complete the sentences below.

   a)   Emulsion paints are **oil-based** / **water-based**.

   b)   Paint dries as the **solvent** / **binding medium** evaporates.

   c)   In oil-based paints the solvent is **oil** / **something that dissolves oil**.

Special Pigments

Q1 Circle the two statements that best describe **thermochromic pigments**.

Change colour when heated.   Change colour when wet.

Change colour in light.

Change colour when cooled.

Change colour in the dark.

Q2 The diagram shows a modern 'glow in the dark' watch.

a) What type of pigment is used on the hands of the watch?
Underline the correct answer.

Thermochromic pigment

Phosphorescent pigment

b) Number these statements 1-4 to explain how the hands on the watch are able to glow in the dark.

☐ It releases the energy over time as light.

☐ It stores the energy.

☐ So it is able to glow in the dark.

☐ The pigment absorbs energy from light.

Q3 **Thermochromic pigments** have many different uses.

Describe **two uses** of thermochromic pigments.
For each use give a **reason** why thermochromic pigments are used.

1. Use ....

Reason ....

....

2. Use ....

Reason ....

....

Top Tip: I used to have a pencil that could glow in the dark — it made it easy to find if it fell down the back of the desk. Only problem was that you couldn't see what you were writing in the dark.

Polymers

Q1 Match each **monomer** with the **polymer** that can be made from it.

styrene	polychloroethene
ethene	polypropene
chloroethene	polystyrene
propene	polyethene

We bring you gold, frankincense...
and poly-myrrh

Q2 Fill in the gaps in the passage below using the following words.

monomers	polymerisation	molecules

Polymers are giant .... made by joining small molecules

called .... together. The reaction that makes polymers

is called ....

Q3 Tick the boxes to show whether each of the following statements is **true** or **false**.

True False

a) Monomers are very large molecules. ☐ ☐

b) Addition polymers are made from alkane monomers. ☐ ☐

c) You can work out the name of a polymer from the type of monomer it's made from. ☐ ☐

d) Addition polymers are made using a high pressure and a catalyst. ☐ ☐

Q4 Tick the box next to the **true** statement below.

☐ The monomer of polyethene is ethene.

☐ The polymer of polyethene is ethane.

☐ The monomer of polyethene is ethane.

Look really carefully at the spellings of the words.

Top Tip: Naming polymers really is as easy as 1, 2, 3. Take the polymerisation of propene. There are lots of molecules of propene, so the polymer's called polypropene. Simple.

Polymers and Their Uses

Q1 From the list below, underline any **properties** a plastic used to make **Wellington boots** should have.

low melting point   waterproof   lightweight   heat-resistant

N.B. Chlorine dissolves spandex

Q2 Complete the table to show the best **use** of each polymer. Use the options in the list.

carrier bags   window frames   disposable cups

POLYMER	PROPERTIES	USE
polystyrene foam	thermal insulator	
polyethene	lightweight	
PVC	strong, durable, rigid	

Each use can only be used once.

Q3 Kate is trying to choose a jacket to take for a week's walking in Wales.

a) Give one advantage of:

i) waterproof clothing. ....

ii) breathable clothing. ....

Kate has the choice between a **coated nylon jacket** or a **GORE-TEX®** jacket. Both jackets are waterproof.

b) Give **two** other properties of the **coated nylon jacket**.

1. ....

2. ....

c) Which jacket should Kate take for a week's walking? Explain your answer.

....

....

Q4 Connect the method of **disposing of plastics** with the **problems** it has. Some problems might be needed more than once.

a)

Burial in landfill sites

Recycling

Burning

sorting out different plastics is difficult and expensive

may release toxic gases that damage the environment

it's a waste of plastic

sites fill up quickly and they're a waste of land

b) Explain why scientists are trying to make biodegradable polymers.

....

....

Module C1 — Carbon Chemistry

Hydrocarbons — Alkanes

You can use this information to help answer some of the questions on this page.

Compound	methane	ethane	propane	butane
Formula	CH_4	C_2H_6	C_3H_8	C_4H_{10}

Q1 Look at the displayed formula of **molecule X**, shown on the right.

a) Is molecule X a hydrocarbon? Explain your answer.

....

....

$$H - \overset{\overset{\displaystyle H}{|}}{C} - \overset{\overset{\displaystyle H}{|}}{\underset{\underset{\displaystyle H}{|}}{C}} - \overset{\overset{\displaystyle H}{|}}{\underset{\underset{\displaystyle H}{|}}{C}} - H$$

Molecule X

b) Give the molecular formula of molecule X.

....

c) What is the name of molecule X? ....

d) The diagrams below show the **structures** of two alkanes. They are unfinished. Complete the diagrams by adding **hydrogen atoms** only. Write the **name** of each compound underneath the diagrams.

i)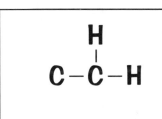

ii)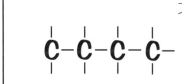

You don't need to add any carbon (C) atoms.

....

....

Q2 Tick the boxes to show if the following statements are **true** or **false**.

		True	False
a)	CH_4 is an alkane.	☐	☐
b)	C_3H_9OH is an alkane.	☐	☐
c)	The carbon atoms in alkanes are joined together by single bonds.	☐	☐
d)	Ethane is an alkane with four carbon atoms.	☐	☐
e)	$CH_3CH_2CH_2CH_3$ is an alkane.	☐	☐
f)	Alkanes are groups of carbon atoms.	☐	☐

Top Tip: These questions on hydrocarbons and alkanes shouldn't be too hard. Just make sure you don't confuse alkanes with alkenes — they're on the next page. Just what you wanted to hear...

Hydrocarbons — Alkenes

You can use this information to help answer some of the questions on this page.

Compound	ethene	propene	butene
Formula	C_2H_4	C_3H_6	C_4H_8

Q1 Complete this table showing the names and displayed formulas of some **alkenes**.

Alkene	Displayed formula
Ethene	**a)**
b)	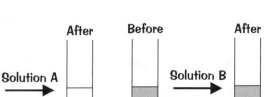

Q2 Tick the boxes to show if the statements are **true** or **false**.

	True	False

a) Alkenes have double bonds between hydrogen atoms. ☐ ☐

b) A double covalent bond means two pairs of electrons are shared. ☐ ☐

c) Alkenes are hydrocarbons. ☐ ☐

d) H−C−C−C=C⟨ is called butene. ☐ ☐

e) H−C−C=C−C−H is not an alkene. ☐ ☐

Q3 Mark has two boiling tubes that contain **bromine water**. He adds some of solution A to one tube and some of solution B to the other. The results are shown on the right.

Before After Before After

Solution A →   Solution B →

a) State what colour bromine water is.

....

b) Tick the box below to show which statement is **true**.

☐ Solution A is an alkene because it turned the bromine water colourless.

☐ Solution B is an alkene because it didn't cause a change in the colour of the bromine water.

Module C1 — Carbon Chemistry

Fractional Distillation of Crude Oil

Q1   Circle the correct answer to each of the following questions.

a)   What type of fuels are crude oil, coal and gas?

> **A — Fossil Fuels**   **B — Renewable Fuels**   **C — Man-made Fuels**

b)   Why is crude oil non-renewable?

> **A — It is impossible to create new oil.**   **B — Oil is very hard to find.**
>
> **C — Oil is being used up faster than it is being formed.**

Q2   Circle the correct words to complete these sentences.

a)   Crude oil is a **mixture** / **compound** of different molecules.

b)   The molecules in crude oil are all **hydrocarbons** / **carbohydrates**.

c)   In fractional distillation the oil is heated until most of it has turned into a **solid** / **gas**.

d)   Hydrocarbons with **high** boiling points leave the column near the **top** / **bottom**.

e)   Hydrocarbons with **low** boiling points leave the column near the **top** / **bottom**.

phwoar... nice tank, love

Q3   **Fractionating columns** are used to separate crude oil into fractions.

Complete this diagram of a fractionating column by:

a)   filling in the labels on the temperature gradient to show which part of the column is **very hot** and which is **cool**.

If you need a hint for this one, think about where the column is heated.

b)   circling the correct fraction that can be collected at each level of the column.

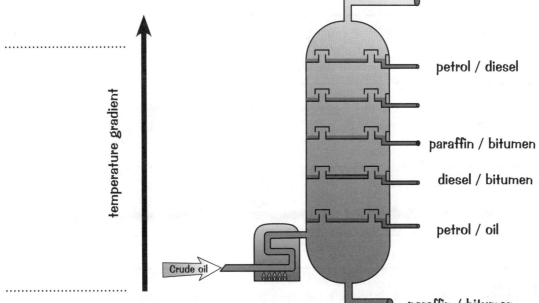

temperature gradient

petrol / diesel

paraffin / bitumen

diesel / bitumen

petrol / oil

Crude oil

paraffin / bitumen

Module C1 — Carbon Chemistry

Fractional Distillation of Crude Oil

Q4   Crude oil is separated into different **fractions** by boiling.

Put these crude oil fractions into order from highest to lowest boiling point.

diesel	naphtha	paraffin	petrol

highest .... **lowest**

Q5   Fractions of crude oil are made up of a **mixture** of substances.

Circle the substance that is **not** found in LPG.

LPG stands for liquefied petroleum gas.

propane   butane   petrol

Q6   The sentences below describe how crude oil is separated by **fractional distillation**.
Fill in the blanks in the sentences using the words below.

fractions	gases	heated	high	low	cooler

A   Crude oil is .... so that most of the hydrocarbons boil.

B   The hot .... rise up the fractionating column.

C   As they rise, the temperature begins to get ....

D   Near the bottom of the column, hydrocarbons with

.... boiling points exit.

E   Near the top of the column, hydrocarbons with .... boiling points exit.

F   In this way crude oil is separated into ....

These are mixtures of a few different hydrocarbons, with similar boiling points.

Top Tip: Fractional distillation can be a tricky idea to get your head round, but once you do you'll be able to answer anything they throw at you. Learn the order of the fractions too, they love that.

Module C1 — Carbon Chemistry

Cracking

Q1 Fill in the gaps using the words below.

high	shorter	longer	catalyst	cracking

There is more need for .... chain fractions of crude oil such

as petrol than for .... chain fractions such as diesel.

Heating long hydrocarbon molecules to .... temperatures

with a .... breaks them down into smaller molecules.

This is called ....

Q2 a) The diagram below shows the apparatus used to crack **paraffin**.
Label the diagram using the words listed below.

gas jar

delivery tube

Bunsen burner

boiling tube

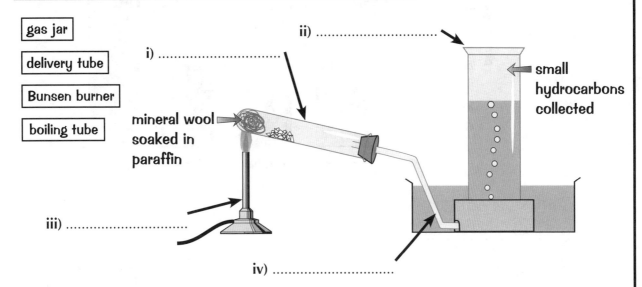

b) Cracking paraffin produces octane and ethene. Which of these substances has the
longest carbon chains? Circle the correct answer.

paraffin   octane   ethene

c) Is cracking usually carried out at **high** or **low** temperatures? ....

d) Name one other condition that is needed for cracking. ....

e) Tick the boxes to show if the following statements are **true** or **false**.

i) Cracking is used to make more petrol.

ii) Cracking is used to make alkenes that are used to make polymers.

iii) Cracking turns small hydrocarbons into larger ones.

True   False

Cracking

Q3   Write the **word equation** for the reaction shown below.

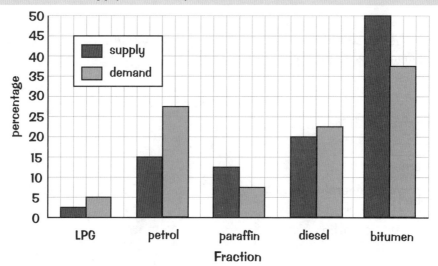

Word equation: .... → .... + ...

Q4   Horatio owns a **crude oil refinery**. He records the amount of each fraction that's present in a sample of crude oil (the **supply**) and compares it to how much his customers want (the **demand**).

a)   What percentage of the supply is:

   i) Petrol? ....

   ii) Bitumen? ....

b)   What percentage of the demand is for:

   i) LPG? ....

   ii) Paraffin? ....

When you have to deal with graph questions like this, it's useful to draw lines from the top of each bar to the axis. This makes it much easier to read off the percentages.

c)   There is more supply than demand for some fractions. Name these fractions.

....

d)   Which fraction is most likely to **run out**?

....

Top Tips: Cracking is really useful, and dead important too. It helps us get the most out of crude oil, so we don't end up with loads of a fraction that we don't want or need. Hooray for cracking.

Module C1 — Carbon Chemistry

Use of Fossil Fuels

Q1   Tick the boxes to show if the following statements are **true** or **false**.

     True   False

a)   Crude oil is only used where it's found.

b)   Transporting crude oil can cause environmental problems.

Q2   Complete the passage using some of the words given below.

detergents	waterproof	cold	slick	toxic

If a tanker carrying crude oil is damaged the oil can spill into the sea creating

an oil .... If the oil gets onto the feathers of birds it stops them

being .... This can cause the birds to die of ....

Sometimes .... are added to spilled oil to try and clean it up, but these

can be .... to wildlife like fish and shellfish.

Q3   Isobella is trying to decide which fuel to use — fuel A or fuel B. She tests their **energy content** by using them to heat 50 cm³ of water from 25 °C to 40 °C. She weighs the fuels before and after heating the water. She records her results in the table below.

Fuel	Starting Mass (g)	Final Mass (g)	Mass of Fuel Burnt (g)
A	98	92	
B	102	89	

Today's Lecture: 'My favourite few Ls'

a)   Complete the table by calculating the mass of each fuel that was burnt.

b)   Which fuel contains more energy per gram? ....

c)   What other things does Isobella need to think about when choosing the best fuel?
Circle the **four** correct answers.

cost   ease of use   colour   storage   availability   smell

Q4   Describe why it is important to think about the following things when choosing the best fuel.

a)   The toxicity of the fuel.

....

b)   The pollution caused by burning the fuel.

....

Burning Fuels

Q1   Hydrocarbons make good **fuels**.

Complete this **general word equation** for completely burning a hydrocarbon in the open air.

hydrocarbon + ... → carbon dioxide + ...

Q2   The apparatus below can be used to show that water and carbon dioxide are produced when **hexane** (a hydrocarbon) is completely burned.

a) What will happen to the limewater if carbon dioxide is produced?

....

b) How would you tell if water is produced?

....

....

....

Q3   **Incomplete combustion** can cause problems.

a) Use the words below to write a general word equation for the **incomplete combustion** of a hydrocarbon.

carbon monoxide   hydrocarbon   water   oxygen   carbon

.... + ... → .... + ... + ...

b) Which releases more energy:

i) complete or incomplete combustion? ....

ii) a blue flame or a yellow flame? Explain your answer. ....

....

c) Tick the boxes to show which of the following statements are **true**.

☐ Carbon monoxide is a poisonous gas.

☐ Incomplete combustion happens when there isn't enough oxygen.

☐ Incomplete combustion produces a clean flame without much soot.

d) Why is it important to check that gas appliances are working properly? ....

....

The Atmosphere

Q1 Draw lines to put the statements in the **right order** on the timeline. One has been done for you.

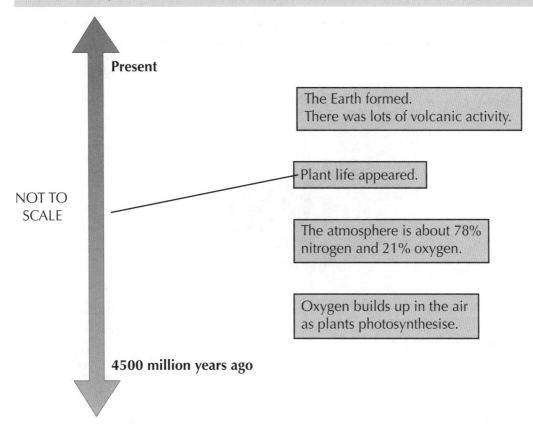

Present

NOT TO
SCALE

The Earth formed.
There was lots of volcanic activity.

Plant life appeared.

The atmosphere is about 78%
nitrogen and 21% oxygen.

Oxygen builds up in the air
as plants photosynthesise.

4500 million years ago

Q2 Tick the boxes next to the sentences below to say if they are **true** or **false**.

		True	False
a)	The atmosphere today contains water vapour.	☐	☐
b)	30% of the atmosphere today is nitrogen.	☐	☐
c)	Carbon dioxide makes up 21% of the atmosphere.	☐	☐

Q3 The sentences below each contain **one** mistake. Write out correct versions of these sentences.

a) 0.035% of the atmosphere today is argon.

....

b) Respiration and combustion decrease the amount of carbon dioxide in the atmosphere.

....

....

c) Photosynthesis and combustion decrease the amount of oxygen in the Earth's atmosphere.

....

....

The Atmosphere

Q4 The Earth's atmosphere today is **very different** to what it was like millions of years ago.

a) The pie chart below shows the amount of different gases in the Earth's atmosphere today. Add the labels '**Nitrogen**', '**Oxygen**', and '**Carbon dioxide and other gases**'.

Earth's Atmosphere Today

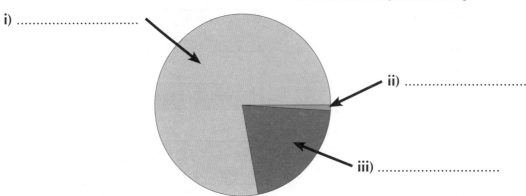

i) ....

ii) ....

iii) ....

b) This pie chart shows the amount of different gases that we think were in the Earth's atmosphere 4500 million years ago.

Earth's Atmosphere 4500 Million Years Ago

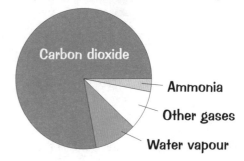

Where did the gases in the **early** atmosphere come from?

....

....

c) Circle the correct words to complete the sentence.

> The levels of oxygen, nitrogen and carbon dioxide in the Earth's atmosphere today **vary greatly / stay pretty much the same.**

d) i) Describe how photosynthesis by plants affects the level of **oxygen** in the atmosphere.

....

....

ii) Describe how photosynthesis by plants affects the level of **carbon dioxide** in the atmosphere.

....

....

The Carbon Cycle

Q1 Here is a diagram of the **carbon cycle**. The processes A, B and C are all **different**.

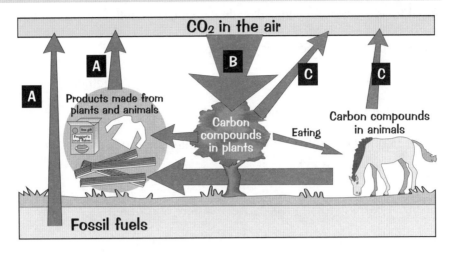

a) What is process A? ....

b) What is process B? ....

c) What is Process C? ....

Q2 Tick the boxes to show what effect photosynthesis, respiration and combustion have on the levels of **carbon dioxide** in the atmosphere.

	Increases CO_2 levels	Decreases CO_2 levels
a) Photosynthesis	☐	☐
b) Respiration	☐	☐
c) Combustion	☐	☐

Combustion just means to burn in oxygen.

Q3 Carbon that was once part of Henry VIII could now be part of you.

Name each process in the diagram.

A ....

B ....

C ....

Carbon is part of Henry VIII → A → CO_2 in the atmosphere → B → Carbon trapped in plants → C → Carbon is part of you

Top Tips: The carbon cycle is one crazy piece of chemistry — where else would you find out that the air you are breathing in right now could have been part of a gorilla, or that the clothes you're wearing might once have been a bit of Queen Victoria's hair... not in an English guide that's for sure.

Module C1 — Carbon Chemistry

Air Pollution and Acid Rain

Q1 Use the words and phrases to complete the sentences below.

a) When fossil fuels are burned **sulfur dioxide** / **magnesium sulfide** is produced.

b) This pollutant comes from the sulfur **ore** / **impurities** in the fuel.

c) Inside a car engine nitrogen and oxygen from the air react together

to make **nitrogen oxides** / **oxygen nitrides**.

d) When sulfur or nitrogen pollutants react with water in clouds they make **acid rain** / **smog**.

Q2 **Pollutants** from burning fossil fuels cause a variety of problems.

a) Circle **two** problems caused by **acid rain** from the choices below.

increases the greenhouse effect   kills plants and animals in lakes

kills trees   causes photochemical smog

b) Tick the correct box to show if the following statements are **true** or **false**.

    True False

i) Nitrogen oxides cause photochemical smog.

ii) Acid rain can cause metals to corrode.

iii) Carbon monoxide isn't poisonous.

c) Explain why building out of limestone in **polluted** cities might **not** be a good idea.

....

Q3 The sentences below each contain **one** mistake. Write out correct versions of these statements.

a) Carbon monoxide is produced by complete combustion.

....

b) Incomplete combustion happens when there is plenty of oxygen.

....

Q4 **Catalytic converters** reduce the amount of harmful gases that are released into the atmosphere.

a) Which gas do catalytic converters change carbon monoxide into? Circle the correct answer.

carbon dioxide   oxygen   nitrogen   sulfur dioxide

b) Give one reason why it is important to control the levels of pollutants in the atmosphere.

....

Module C1 — Carbon Chemistry

Mixed Questions — Module C1

Q1   Brian is making a sponge cake. He puts **baking powder** in the mixture to make the cake 'rise'.

a)   Baking powder contains sodium hydrogencarbonate. Its formula is $NaHCO_3$.
How many **oxygen** atoms does a molecule of sodium hydrogencarbonate contain?

....

b)   Brian's cake rises because a **gas** is produced when the baking powder is heated.
Use the chemical formulas below to write a symbol equation for the reaction
which produces this gas.

$$H_2O \qquad 2NaHCO_3 \qquad CO_2 \qquad Na_2CO_3$$

.... $\rightarrow$ .... + ... + ...

c)   Are the chemical changes that take place when a cake is baked **reversible** or **irreversible**?
Underline the correct answer.

reversible   irreversible

Q2   Pentane is a hydrocarbon. Pentane can be **cracked** to give propane and ethene.

pentane   →   propane   +   ethene

a)   List **two** conditions that are usually used for cracking.

1. ....

2. ....

b)   Name one **fuel** that cracking can help increase the supply of.

....

c)   Ethene is used in polymerisation reactions.
Name the **product** formed from the polymerisation of ethene.

....

d)   Label the diagrams below to show which structure is the **monomer** and which is the **polymer**.

i) ....   ii) ....

e)   Give one **use** of the polymer formed from ethene.

....

Mixed Questions — Module C1

Q3   **Perfumes** and **nail varnish** are both types of cosmetic.

a)   Synthetic perfumes often contain **esters**.
The reaction for making an ester is shown below. Identify the reactants and products.

$$acid + alcohol \rightarrow ester + water$$

Reactants: ....   Products: ....

b)   Suggest why it is important that a perfume is non-toxic.

....

....

c)   Nail varnish remover dissolves nail varnish. Tick the boxes
to show if the statements below are **true** or **false**.

True   False

i)   Nail varnish remover is the solute.

ii)   The nail varnish is soluble in nail varnish remover.

iii) The nail varnish is the solvent.

iv) The nail varnish and nail varnish remover make a solution.

NO MORE
NAIL
VARNISH

Q4   **Fuel X** is a hydrocarbon that can be burnt to release energy.
A company is trying to decide whether or not to use fuel X to power its machinery.

a)   Give **two** properties, other than energy value, that the company
should take into account when deciding whether or not to use fuel X.

1. ....

2. ....

b)   Fuel X is burnt in **plenty of oxygen** and in **low oxygen** conditions. Join the **conditions** used to the
products made when fuel X is burnt. Some products might be needed in both conditions.

carbon

in plenty of oxygen   carbon monoxide

This question is asking
about complete and
incomplete combustion.

in low oxygen   carbon dioxide

water

c)   A scientist burns a small amount of the fuel to find out its energy value.
He burns it in plenty of oxygen. Underline the colour the flame will be.

blue   yellow

Module C1 — Carbon Chemistry

Mixed Questions — Module C1

Q5 Crude oil is a mixture of hydrocarbons. It can be separated into useful fractions by **fractional distillation**.

a) Which fraction has the higher boiling point? Underline the correct answer.

paraffin   **diesel**   **LPG**

b) Circle the correct words in the paragraph below to explain how crude oil is separated.

> The crude oil is heated and fed into the bottom of the fractionating column. There is a temperature gradient which means it is **hot / cold** at the bottom and **hotter / cooler** at the top. This means hydrocarbons with **high / low** boiling points leave at the bottom and hydrocarbons with **high / low** boiling points leave at the top.

c) Crude oil is often transported in large **tanker ships**. Describe an environmental problem this can cause.

....

....

Q6 The atmosphere of **Mars** is 95.3% carbon dioxide, 2.7% nitrogen, and 2% of other gases.

a) The Earth's atmosphere contains nitrogen, oxygen and carbon dioxide. In what percentages are they found?

Nitrogen ....

Oxygen ....

Carbon dioxide ....

b) Describe **two** differences between the atmosphere of Mars and the atmosphere of the Earth.

1. ....

2. ....

Q7 A tub of ice cream contains an **emulsifier** and a **food colouring**.

a) Explain why an emulsifier has been added to the ice cream.

....

....

b) Explain why food colouring has been added to the ice cream.

....

Heat

Q1   Complete these sentences by circling the correct word from each pair.

Heat is a measure of **hotness** / **energy**.

Temperature is a measure of **hotness** / **energy**.

Heat travels from a **hot** / **cold** place to a **hot** / **cold** place.

The hotter something is, the **slower** / **faster** it will cool.

When a substance is heated its particles vibrate **more** / **less** quickly.

Temperature / **Heat** is measured in °C.

Temperature / **Heat** is measured in J.

Q2   Three flasks, each containing the same amount of water at the same temperature, are left to cool in **different rooms**.

Room A 20°C   Room B 22°C   Room C 24°C

Water 60°C   Water 60°C   Water 60°C

Which flask will cool **fastest**?
Give a reason for your answer.

Flask .... will cool fastest because ....

....

Q3   A **thermogram** can show where heat energy is escaping from a house.

a)   Look at the thermogram of three houses **X**, **Y** and **Z** below.
For each description below, write the correct letter **X**, **Y** or **Z** in the box.

X   Y   Z

KEY:

coldest ⟶ hottest

i)   This house has a cold roof and windows, but hot walls.   ☐

ii) This house has cold windows and walls, but a hot roof.   ☐

iii) This house has a cold roof and walls, but hot windows.   ☐

b)   The higher the temperature, the more heat is escaping from that part of the house.

Which house is losing most heat through its **roof**? **X**, **Y** or **Z**?   ☐

Specific Heat Capacity

Q1 Different substances can have different **specific heat capacities**.

a) What is **specific heat capacity**? Circle the correct statement below.

> A — The difference in temperature between the substance and the air around it.

> B — The amount of energy needed to make 1 kg of a substance rise in temperature by 1 °C.

> C — The amount of energy needed to melt 1 kg of a solid.

b) Agatha has 1 kg samples of two substances — A and B. Substance **A** has a **higher** specific heat capacity than substance B. Both samples cool down by 10 °C. Which will release more heat — A or B? Circle the correct answer.

> Substance A

> Substance B

Q2 Jenny wants to do an experiment to measure how much **energy** it takes to warm 250 ml of water by **15 °C**. She sets up the apparatus below.

a) What is the standard unit of energy? ....

b) Label Jenny's apparatus.

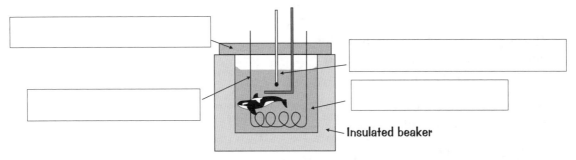

Insulated beaker

c) Describe how Jenny can use this apparatus to do her experiment.

Think about you'd measure with each piece of apparatus

....

....

....

Q3 **Mercury** has a specific heat capacity of **139 J/kg°C**.
2 litres of mercury has a mass of around **27 kg**.

Work out the energy released by **2 litres** of mercury cooling from **70 °C** to **20 °C**.

Energy = mass × SHC × temperature change.

....

....

....

Melting and Boiling

Q1 The graph shows the temperature change as a substance is heated up.
The letters A to E represent each **state** of the substance and each **change of state**.

Draw lines to join each state or change of state to the correct letter.

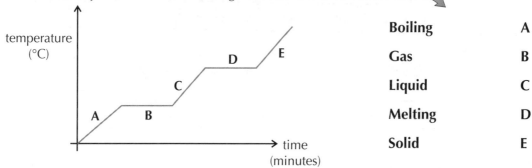

Boiling	A
Gas	B
Liquid	C
Melting	D
Solid	E

Q2 A beaker of pure water is heated. When it reaches 100 °C it **stays** at 100 °C, even though it is **still being heated**. Which of sentences A to D is the correct explanation for why this happens? Circle the **one** correct letter.

A Energy is being lost to the surroundings as quickly as it is being supplied to the beaker.

B The pan is absorbing the extra energy.

C The energy supplied is being used to change the water to steam.

D A more powerful heater should have been used.

Q3 The graph shows what happens to the temperature of a beaker of hot **liquid wax** as it cools to room temperature.

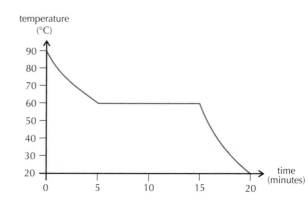

a) At what temperature does the wax start to become **solid**? ....

b) How can you tell?

....

....

Q4 The **specific latent heat** of melting for an ice lolly is **334 000 J/kg**.

a) What does **specific latent heat of melting** mean?

....

....

b) Calculate the amount of energy needed to melt **0.01 kg** of the ice lolly at 0 °C.

Energy = mass × SLH.

.... J

Top Tips: Mmm... ice lollies, just what you need with all this talk of heating up.
Remember, if something is melting or boiling there's **no** temperature change — weird but true.

Conduction and Convection in the Home

Q1 Draw lines to match each type of heat transfer with the correct explanation of how it works.

Conduction

Vibrating particles pass on energy to the particles next to them.

Convection

Particles with more energy move to a cooler place, taking their heat energy with them.

Q2 Tick to show whether the sentences below are **true** or **false**.
Write a correct version of any false statements in the space below.

True False

a) Conduction involves **energy** passing between **vibrating particles**. ☐ ☐

b) **Metals** are very **poor** conductors. ☐ ☐

c) **Solids** are usually better **conductors** of heat than liquids and gases. ☐ ☐

d) **Air** is a **good** insulator. ☐ ☐

....

....

Q3 Jacob says, "My radiator heats the air in my room by **radiation**."

a) Why is Jacob wrong?

....

....

b) Use the words below to complete the passage.

rises	falls	spread

Radiators can .... warm air around a whole room.

When air is heated, it .... above any colder air.

The cooler air .... to take its place.

Q4 Great Aunt Marjorie knits blankets for babies. She says that a blanket **with holes** in keeps a baby **warmer** than a blanket without holes in. Why is this?

....

....

....

....

The holes contain air rather than wool. Think about why this would reduce heat flow.

Module P1 — Energy for the Home

Heat Radiation

Q1 Tick the sentences below to show whether they are **true** or **false**.

True   False

a) The hotter a surface is, the more heat it emits.　☐　☐

b) Heat is radiated as ultraviolet waves.　☐　☐

c) All hot objects absorb and emit heat radiation.　☐　☐

d) When a surface absorbs heat radiation, its temperature may rise.　☐　☐

e) The amount of heat radiation absorbed by a surface depends only on its colour.　☐　☐

Q2 Complete the following sentences by circling the correct word from each pair.

a) Dark, dull surfaces are **good / poor** absorbers and **good / poor** emitters of heat radiation.

b) The best surfaces for reflecting heat are **shiny / dull**.

c) White surfaces are **good / poor** absorbers.

Q3 Paul is making toast with sausages for tea. He toasts the bread in the **toaster** and puts the sausages under the **grill**.

You're far too young to be smoking.

a) How is **energy transferred** from the toaster to the surface of the bread?
Circle the one correct word from the list below.

conduction　　　　　convection　　　　　radiation

b) Paul lines his grill pan with **shiny foil**. How does this **help him** to grill his sausages?
Circle the one correct explanation below.

A — The shiny surface absorbs the heat conducted from the grill.

B — The shiny surface helps the heat flow by convection.

C — The shiny surface reflects the heat radiation back on to the sausages.

Q4 Mr Jones and Ms Smith each put a **solar hot water panel** on the roof of their houses.

solar hot water panels

Explain why Ms Smith gets more hot water than Mr Jones.

Ms Smith's house

Mr Jones' house

....

....

Saving Energy

Q1 Draw lines to match up the **words** with their **meanings**.

Initial cost

Cost-effectiveness

Payback time

Annual saving

How much money you save on bills each year.

How much you have to pay at the start.

How long it takes to save as much as you spent initially.

How worthwhile it is to spend the money.

Q2 Heat is lost from a house through its **roof**, **walls**, **doors** and **windows**.

a) In the spaces on the diagram, write down **one** way to reduce heat loss through each part of the house. An example has been done for you.

through the roof

....

....

through the walls

....

....

through the windows

Thick curtains

....

b) Name one other way to reduce heat loss through **windows**. ....

Describe how it reduces heat loss by conduction, convection or radiation.

....

....

....

Top Tips: Saving energy in the home is mostly to do with reducing heat loss — so making sure you don't have to use more energy to make more heat to replace the stuff you've lost. It doesn't have to be expensive — even a thicker pair of curtains at the window will help a bit.

Saving Energy

Q3 Circle the correct words in each pair in the sentences below to explain how the following types of insulation work.

a) **Cavity wall insulation**:

Cavity walls have a gap between two layers of bricks which reduces **conduction** / **convection**. Insulating foam or **broken glass** / **fibreglass** is put in the gap to trap **air** / **water** to reduce convection.

b) **Loft insulation**:

Fibreglass, mineral or rock 'wool' laid across the loft floor reduces **convection** / **conduction** through the ceiling into the roof space because it's a poor **conductor** / **insulator**.

c) **Double glazing**:

Window panes have two layers of glass with a gap between them filled with **wax** / **air**. This reduces **conduction** / **radiation** between the layers of glass.

Q4 **Draught-proofing** can reduce heat loss around doors and windows. Circle the correct statement below to explain how it does this.

A — Foam and plastic strips are poor conductors, so they remove heat from doors and windows, keeping them warm.

B — Strips of foam and plastic stop hot air escaping from the gaps around doors and windows, which reduces convection.

C — Foam and plastic strips emit heat radiation back into the room to heat it up.

Q5 Mr Tarantino wants to buy a **hot water tank jacket** to save on his heating bills, but his friend tells him that **loft insulation** would be more **cost-effective**.

	Hot water tank jacket	Loft insulation
Initial Cost	£60	£200
Annual Saving	£15	£100
Payback time	4 years	

a) Calculate the **payback time** for loft insulation and write it in the table.

payback time = initial cost ÷ annual saving

b) i) Is his friend right? Circle the correct answer.   **yes**   **no**

ii) Give a reason for your answer.

....

....

Efficiency

Q1 Choose from the words in the box below to complete the paragraph.

light	efficiency	wasted

A lamp transfers electrical energy into useful .... energy.

Some of the electrical energy is .... as heat energy.

The .... of the lamp is the amount of useful energy

divided by the total energy supplied.

Q2 Here is an **energy flow diagram** for an electric lamp. Complete the following sentences.

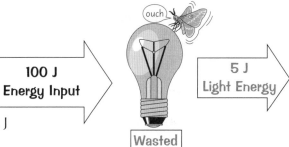

a) The **total energy supplied** is .... J

b) The **energy usefully transferred** is .... J

c) The amount of energy **wasted** is ....

.... J

d) The **efficiency** of the lamp is ....

Efficiency = (Useful ÷ Total) × 100% .... %

Q3 a) Complete the **blanks** in the table below.

Appliance	Total Energy Supplied (J)	Energy Usefully Transferred (J)	Wasted Energy (J)	Efficiency (%)
A	2000	1000	1000	
B	10 000		7000	
C	4000	1000		
D	20 000	2000	18 000	

b) Circle the letter of the **most efficient** appliance in the table.

Sankey Diagrams

Q1 The sketch below is a **Sankey diagram** for a blender.

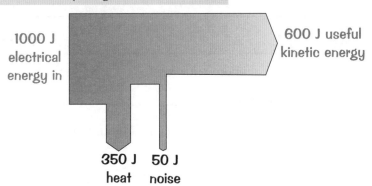

1000 J electrical energy in

600 J useful kinetic energy

350 J heat   50 J noise

a) Circle the correct word to complete the sentence:

The thicker the arrow on a Sankey diagram, the more **energy / efficiency** is being transferred.

b) What is the **efficiency** of the blender? Give your answer as a **decimal**.

Efficiency = Useful ÷ Total

....

....

c) In what **form** is the **most** energy lost? ....

Q2 Professor Bean is testing a new car engine.
For every **100 J** of energy supplied to the engine, **50 J** are transformed into **useful kinetic energy**, **10 J** are **wasted** as **sound energy** and **the rest** is wasted as **heat energy**.

a) On the grid below, complete the **Sankey diagram** to show his results.

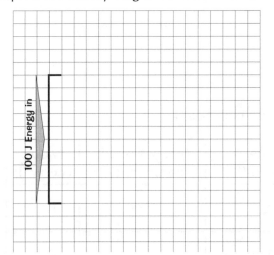

Use one square for every 10 J of energy.

100 J Energy in

b) What is the **efficiency** of the new car engine? Give your answer as a **decimal**.

....

....

Top Tips: Sankey diagrams and efficiency go hand in hand. They help you picture how energy efficient something is — a big 'wasted energy' arrow means it's probably not very efficient.

Wave Basics

Q1 Use the following words to label the different parts of the wave below.

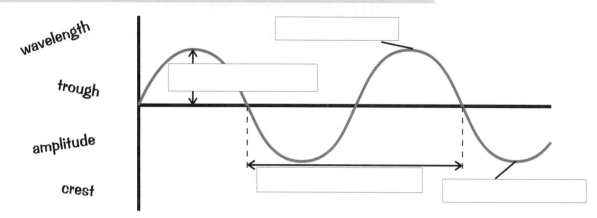

wavelength

trough

amplitude

crest

Q2 Complete the sentences by circling the correct word from each pair.

a) **Some / All** electromagnetic waves travel at the same speed in space.

b) The speed of a wave is equal to its **amplitude / frequency** multiplied by its **wavelength / frequency**.

c) Frequency is the number of **waves / amplitudes** per **second / wavelength**.

Q3 Diagrams A, B and C represent electromagnetic waves.

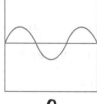

| **A** | **B** | **C** |

a) Which two diagrams show waves with the same **frequency**? ...... and ......

b) Which two diagrams show waves with the same **amplitude**? ...... and ......

c) Which two diagrams show waves with the same **wavelength**? ...... and ......

Q4 A pebble is dropped into still water. Waves move out across the surface of the water. The wavelength is **0.016 m** and the waves are generated at a rate of **10 a second**.

a) What is the **frequency** of the waves in Hz? ....

b) Calculate the **speed** of the waves.

Speed = frequency × wavelength.

....

.... m/s

Top Tips:
I got really excited about this page until I realised it had nothing to do with Mexicans or surfing. Make sure you know the meanings of all the words to do with waves and you can use the wave equation to work out speed. After that you'll be waving your cares goodbye.

Module P1 — Energy for the Home

Wave Properties

Q1 Harriet spends at least an hour looking at herself in a **mirror** every day.
The image she sees is formed from light reflected by the mirror.

Complete the diagram to show an incident ray of light being reflected by the mirror.
Label the **angle of incidence**, **i**, the **normal**, and the **angle of reflection**, **r**.

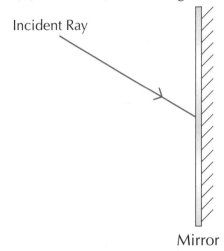

Incident Ray

Mirror

Q2 Tick the boxes to show whether these statements are **true** or **false**.
Write out a correct version of any false statements in the space below.

True   **False**

a) Electromagnetic waves travel in **curved lines** through **different substances**.   ☐   ☐

b) The **normal** is at right angles to the **surface**.   ☐   ☐

c) The **angle of incidence** is always equal to the **angle of reflection**.   ☐   ☐

....

....

Q3 José uses a simple **periscope** to see light rays coming from objects behind him.
The periscope contains two angled mirrors to bend the light into his eyes.

Complete the ray diagram below to show how this works.

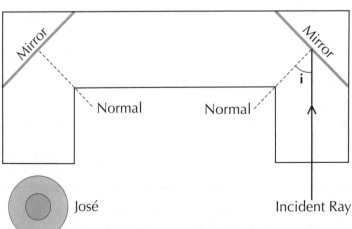

Mirror   Mirror

Normal   Normal   **i**

José   Incident Ray

Diffraction and Refraction

Q1 An important property of waves is **diffraction**.

a) Circle the correct word from each pair below to explain what **diffraction** means.

Diffraction is where a wave **slows down** / **spreads out** as it passes

through a **gap** / **different substance** or when it meets an obstacle in its path.

b) A ripple tank is used to study diffraction of waves through gaps.

In ① there's a small gap that would cause **lots** of diffraction.

In ② there's a larger gap that would cause much **less** diffraction.

Complete both diagrams to show what happens to the waves after they pass through the gap.

 ①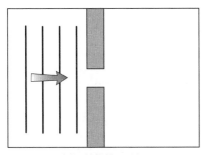

Lots of diffraction

②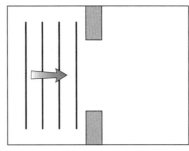

Little diffraction

Q2 Diagrams A and B show waves travelling from one substance to another.

A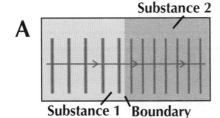

B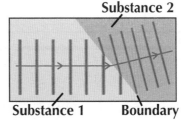

a) Which diagram shows the waves being **refracted**? ....

b) Why does refraction **not happen** in the other diagram?

....

c) Tick **one** box that explains why waves refract at boundaries.

☐ Because the waves change colour.

☐ Because the waves change speed.

☐ Because the waves change temperature.

FACT: Chameleons change colour to stay on-trend in the fashion world. This season they are mostly wearing grey.

EM Waves and Communication

Q1 Draw a line to match each type of wave shown below with a **technology** it can be used for.

Visible light

TV and radio transmissions

Radio waves

Mobile phones

Microwaves

Broadband internet

Q2 Here are four different types of **electromagnetic wave**:

| ultraviolet | microwaves | X-rays | infrared |

a) Which has the **lowest frequency**? ....

b) Which has the **shortest wavelength**? ....

Q3 Electromagnetic (EM) radiation occurs at many different wavelengths.

Complete the table by putting the seven types of EM waves in order of frequency:

Ultraviolet   Infrared   X-rays   Gamma rays   Radio waves   Microwaves

| | | | VISIBLE LIGHT | | | |

Increasing Frequency

Q4 **Radio telescopes** are used to pick up radio waves which are then used to create **images**. The telescopes need to be very large, or else the images are 'fuzzy' and lack detail.

a) Circle the correct words in each pair to complete the sentences below.

The size of a receiver is linked to the **speed** / **wavelength** of the wave.

The larger the **speed** / **wavelength**, the **smaller** / **larger** the receiver needs to be.

b) Which would need to be **larger** — a receiver for infrared or one for visible light? Circle the correct answer.

infrared   visible light

c) Explain your answer to part **b**).

....

....

Communicating with Light and Infrared

Q1 Circle the correct words in each pair to complete each of the sentences below.

a) Lasers produce a beam of **light** / **X-rays**.

b) All the waves in a laser beam are of a single **colour** / **pitch**.

c) Lasers have **narrow** / **wide** beams that **spread out** / **stay narrow** a long distance away from the source of the beam.

Q2 Light and infrared waves can be **used** in many different ways.

a) Draw lines to join up each of the boxes on the left with its correct use.

Visible light   Cutting tools

Lasers   Automatic doors

Infrared   Morse code

b) Give **three other** uses of lasers:

1. ....

2. ....

3. ....

Q3 **Morse code** was historically used for communication.

Each of the statements below contain **one mistake**.
Write a correct version of each statement in the space below.

a) Morse code is a type of **analogue** signal.

....

b) Morse code works by using pulses of **gamma rays**.

....

c) Signals can be sent over **short** distances using Morse code.

....

Top Tips: Visible light is the EM wave we're most familiar with, so it's easy to take it for granted. Even before all the new communication technologies were invented, people were using light in a simple but useful way to communicate over long distances — although flashing a light on and off isn't **quite** as handy as a quick text to tell your mum you'll be home for tea.

Communicating with Light and Infrared

Q4 **Infrared** radiation is used in **remote controls** for electrical devices.

a) Complete the paragraph below, choosing from the words in the box.

pattern	control	pulses

A remote controls emits .... of infrared which act

as a code to .... an electrical device such as a TV.

For example, a DVD player may be programmed to know that a certain

.... of pulses means stop, so if it receives this it will stop.

b) Besides remote controls, write down **one other** use of infrared radiation in communications.

....

....

Q5 Tick the boxes to show whether these statements are **true** or **false**. **True False**

a) Infrared radiation can be used to send information between phones. ☐ ☐

b) Infrared is too dangerous to be used in the home. ☐ ☐

c) Infrared radiation is also known as heat radiation. ☐ ☐

d) Automatic doors use infrared radiation. ☐ ☐

e) Infrared radiation can't be used in optical fibres. ☐ ☐

Q6 Infrared sensors can be used in **security systems**.

Circle the one correct statement below that explains why infrared can be used.

A — Intruders would give off infrared radiation that can be picked up by sensors which detect body heat, even if the person can't be seen.

B — Light waves reflect off people and on to the infrared sensor, allowing them to be seen on the security system.

C — Infrared sensors emit heat radiation to make it too hot for someone to break in to a building.

Optical Fibres

Q1   Choose from the words below to complete the passage.

boundary	reflected	internal	infrared

Optical fibres use total .... reflection.

Visible light or .... waves are sent down the fibre and

are .... when they hit the .... between the layers.

Q2   Tick to show whether these statements are **true** or **false**.

                                                                  True False

a)   Light and infrared waves travel **really fast** in optical fibres.   ☐   ☐

b)   Optical fibres work because the light signal is **reflected** along the fibre.   ☐   ☐

c)   For the signal to be transmitted, the rays must enter the fibre
     at an angle **smaller** than the critical angle.   ☐   ☐

Q3   The diagrams show rays of light in an **optical fibre**.
Draw arrows to match each diagram to the correct description of what is happening.

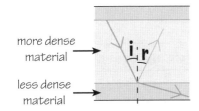

more dense material →

less dense material →

Total internal reflection

Most of the light passes
out of the optical fibre, but
some is reflected internally.

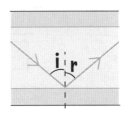

Ray goes along the
surface with some
internal reflection.

Q4   Tick the correct box to explain what is meant by the
critical angle for a boundary between two materials.

☐   The angle of incidence needed for reflection of a ray to occur.

☐   The angle of incidence above which total internal reflection of a ray will occur.

☐   The angle of incidence needed for refraction of a ray to occur.

Wireless Communication

Q1 Circle the correct words to complete each of the sentences below.

a) Radio waves can travel long distances because they **reflect** / **radiate** off a part of the atmosphere.

b) **Reflection** / **Refraction** can be **good** / **bad** for communications because it
can bend signals away from receivers, so the signal is **stronger** / **lost**.

Q2 Lots of things use **wireless technology**, like **mobile phones**.

a) Write down **two other** uses of wireless technology.

1. ....

2. ....

b) Give **two advantages** of wireless technology.

1. ....

2. ....

The new NV 883 — wireless,
all singing, all dancing.

Q3 Wendy listens to a radio talk show on a **digital radio** in her lounge. She then goes out
into the garden and listens to the same radio talk show on a **portable analogue radio**.

a) The voices of the radio talk show host and their guests sound much **clearer** on the **digital** radio
than they do on the analogue radio. Circle the correct statement below to explain this.

A — Digital signals suffer from less interference than analogue signals.

B — Digital signals are broadcast at a louder volume than analogue signals.

b) Give **one other advantage** of digital audio broadcasting (DAB).

....

c) Give **one disadvantage** of DAB.

....

....

Q4 Rebekah listens to 'Rock Radio' which broadcasts an analogue signal at 1152 kHz.
A new radio station called 'Banjo Breakdown' starts broadcasting an analogue signal at 1155 kHz.
Suggest why Rebekah might not be able to hear 'Rock Radio' as clearly anymore.

....

Hint — the frequencies
of the two analogue
signals are very similar.

....

....

Microwaves

Q1 Tick the boxes to show whether the following statements are **true** or **false**.   **True**   **False**

a) Mobile phones use microwave signals. ☐ ☐

b) It is definitely safe to use mobile phones. ☐ ☐

c) Microwaves can't be absorbed by water molecules. ☐ ☐

d) Microwaves can penetrate a few centimetres into food. ☐ ☐

e) Microwave signals can be affected by bad weather. ☐ ☐

f) Microwaves can diffract around large obstacles such as a large block of flats. ☐ ☐

Q2 Mr Schwarzenegger and Mr Stallone are arguing about a **mobile phone mast** being put up near their homes.

a) Mr Stallone wants the mast to be put up.
Give **one advantage** to having the mast put up.

....

b) Mr Schwarzenegger says, 'A mobile mast near our homes would **definitely** damage our health.'

i) Is he right?   **yes**   **no**

ii) Explain your answer.

....

Q3 Sharon is heating up some **ready-made curry** in her **microwave** oven.

a) Briefly explain how microwaves heat up the curry.

....

....

....

b) The curry comes in a **plastic** container.
Explain why Sharon can leave the curry in its container and her curry will still cook.

....

....

c) Microwave ovens have a **metal lining** to stop microwaves getting out.
What effect does this have on the microwaves? Circle the correct answer below.

    A   They're **absorbed** by the metal lining

    B   They're **reflected** by the metal lining

    C   They're **transmitted** by the metal lining

Analogue and Digital Signals

Q1   Devices X and Y both transmit information as signals.
One transmits **analogue** signals, and the other transmits **digital** signals.

   a) Which type of signal can only take one of two values?
   Circle the correct answer below.

   analogue   digital   both

   b) Which type of signal can vary continuously?
   Circle the correct answer below.

   analogue   digital   both

   Signal from Device X

   Signal from Device Y

   c) Which device (X or Y) emits an analogue signal? ....

   d) Which device emits a digital signal? ....

   e) The signal from Device X can be written as a string of **values**.
   Circle the string of values below that best matches the signal shown above for Device X.

   010101   222122   00000

Q2   Fill in the blanks, using the words below.

   analogue   digital   signals   noise   different   radio   easier

   Information can be sent as .... These can either be analogue or

   .... The two types work in .... ways.

   Digital signals can be better than analogue signals because it's ....

   to remove .... from digital signals. This benefit makes digital signals

   much better for .... broadcasts and TV.

Q3   Anna is sitting on a log listening to cheesy tunes on her **analogue** radio.

   a) What values can an analogue signal take?

   ....

   b) Anna is getting a new digital radio for her birthday.
   How many values can a digital signal take? Tick the correct box.

   1 ☐   2 ☐   3 ☐   4 ☐

   c) How are these values usually written? ....

Humans and the Environment

Q1 Spending too much time in the **Sun** gives us a higher risk of **skin cancer**.

a) Which part of the radiation from the Sun causes the damage?
Circle the correct answer.

        Ultraviolet   **Visible light**   **Infrared**

b) Give **two other** health problems this radiation can cause.

1. ....

2. ....

Q2 Marie has **darker skin** than her friend, so she has slightly more protection from harmful radiation.

a) **How** does darker skin give this protection?

....

....

Think about how much radiation is absorbed.

b) i) Marie uses a sun cream with **'SPF 25'** on the label. What does 'SPF 25' mean?

....

....

ii) If Marie normally burns after **30 minutes** in the sun, how many **hours** will she be able to stay in the sun for after applying the sun cream?

....

....

Q3 Scientists discovered a '**hole**' in the **ozone layer** over **Antarctica**.

a) How does the ozone layer help protect life on Earth?

....

....

b) How did the scientists make sure their findings were **accurate**?
Tick the boxes next to the **two** correct answers below.

☐ They carried out just one study.

☐ They used lots of different equipment.

☐ They carried out many different studies.

☐ They didn't tell anyone about their results.

Module P1 — Energy for the Home

Seismic Waves

Q1   Read the following sentences and **underline** the correct word from each highlighted pair.

Earthquakes produce **electromagnetic** / **seismic** waves.

These waves can travel **inside the Earth** / **out into space**.

These waves are also called **shock** / **light** waves.

Q2   Earthquakes can cause damage to the Earth's **surface**.

Name **two other** major problems that Earthquakes can cause.

1. ....

2. ....

Q3   Earthquakes can produce both **S-waves** and **P-waves**.

a)   Tick the boxes to show whether the following statements apply to **S-waves**, **P-waves**, or **both**.

	S	P	Both
i) They're **longitudinal** waves.	☐	☐	☐
ii) They're **transverse** waves.	☐	☐	☐
iii) They can travel through **liquids**.	☐	☐	☐
iv) They can travel through **solids**.	☐	☐	☐

b)   Which travel **faster**, S-waves or P-waves? ....

Q4   Circle the letters next to any of these statements which are **true**.

A   Earthquakes are detected by seismometers.

B   The vibrations in a longitudinal wave are along the same direction that it travels.

C   The vibrations in a transverse wave are at right angles to the direction it travels.

D   Tsunamis are recorded on seismographs.

Top Tips: You'll probably be asked the difference between P-waves and S-waves in your exam, especially which one travels through what. You might even be asked how they're caused and what damage earthquakes can do. There's quite a bit to get your head around, so don't wait a moment longer. Learn your P's and S's, and let seismic waves rock your world, maybe.

Mixed Questions — Module P1

Q1   Jake shows his friend Peter that he can change the TV channel by pointing the remote control at a mirror on the opposite wall.

a) What property of waves does this show? Circle the correct answer.

   reflection   **refraction**   **diffraction**

b) What type of EM wave is used in the remote control? Circle the correct answer.

   infrared   **visible light**   **X-rays**

Q2   Steve has bought a new fridge. It has a thermometer inside, level with the top shelf.

a) Steve puts a hot pie on the **bottom shelf** of the fridge and the temperature on the **top shelf** rises.

Putting hot food in a fridge isn't a great idea — it warms everything else up a little bit.

   i) Numbers the steps below 1-3 to explain how this happens.

   ☐ The warm air rises to the top shelf, taking its heat energy with it.

   ☐ The hot pie heats the cold air on the bottom shelf.

   ☐ The temperature increases on the top shelf because it contains warmer air.

   ii) What is the **name** of this type of heat flow?

   ....

b) Most fridges have a light which comes on when the door is opened. The light in Steve's new fridge wastes 68 J of energy for every 100 J of useful output energy. Calculate the light's efficiency.

Efficiency = (Useful ÷ Total) × 100%

   ....

   .... %

Q3   My landline telephone is connected to the telephone exchange by **optical fibres**.

a) What **type** of EM wave might be sent from the exchange? ....

b) Complete the diagram below to show how an optical fibre works.

c) My mobile phone is **wireless** but also uses EM waves. What type of EM wave is used for mobile phone signals? ....

Mixed Questions — Module P1

Q4 Erik investigates ways of saving energy in his grandma's house. He calculates the annual savings that could be made on his grandma's fuel bills and the cost of doing the work.

Work needed	Annual Saving (£)	Initial Cost (£)	Payback Time (yrs)
Hot water tank jacket	15	15	
Draught-proofing	15	90	
Cavity wall insulation	100	150	

a) Complete the table above by calculating the **payback time** for each of the ways of saving energy.

payback time = initial cost ÷ annual saving

b) Which of the three ways to save energy is the most cost-effective? Circle the correct answer from the list below.

hot water tank jacket   **draught-proofing**   **cavity wall insulation**

c) Give a reason for your answer to part **b)**.

....

....

d) Erik's grandma likes to have a hot bath in the evenings. How much energy is needed to heat 90 kg of water from 14 °C to 36 °C ? (The specific heat capacity of water is 4200 J/kg°C.)

Energy = mass × SHC × temperature change.

....

....

.... J

e) Erik goes on an Arctic expedition. He has to melt 10 kg of snow (at 0 °C) for drinking water. How much energy does he need to melt the snow? (The specific latent heat of water for melting is 334 000 J/kg.)

Energy = mass × SLH.

....

....

.... J

Mixed Questions — Module P1

Q5 Waves A, B and C represent **infrared**, **visible light** and **ultraviolet** (UV) radiation (not in that order). They are all drawn to the same scale.

a) Which of the waves has the greatest **amplitude**? ....

b) Which of the waves has the highest **frequency**? ....

c) Which of the waves represents **UV** radiation? ....

d) What is the name of the part of the atmosphere that protects us from UV radiation from sunlight?

....

Q6 Radio Roary transmits **long-wave** signals with a wavelength of **1500 m** and a frequency of **200 000 Hz**.

Speed = frequency × wavelength

a) Calculate the **speed** of Radio Roary's wave signals.

....

....

b) Mr Potts is on holiday in the Scottish Highlands. His cottage is surrounded by mountains. He can listen to Radio Roary but can't get a signal on his mobile phone. Circle the correct statement to explain this.

A — There are no mobile phone transmitters in Scotland.

B — Mobile phones use microwaves, which can't bend around the mountains like radio waves can.

C — The radio waves used in mobile phones are affected by bad weather.

c) Radio Piracy broadcasts at a **similar frequency** to Radio Roary. They both use **analogue** signals.

i) Why might this affect the sound quality of both stations?

....

....

ii) What can radio stations do to improve their sound quality? Circle the correct answer.

Use DAB   **Use Lasers**   **Use Morse Code**

d) Mr Potts' holiday cottage has a microwave oven. The seal is broken, so he's not allowed to use it. Explain what could happen if he **does** use the broken microwave oven.

....

....

Classification

Q1 Organisms can be **classified** into different groups.

a) Using the words in the box below, fill in the missing labels on the diagram to show the names of the different groups.

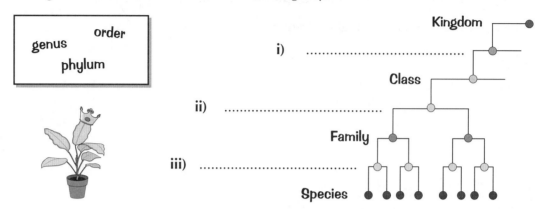

order
genus
phylum

i) .... Kingdom

Class

ii) ....

Family

iii) ....

Species

b) Circle the correct word to complete the sentence below.

Living things are divided into groups based on their **height / characteristics / personalities.**

c) What things can classification help us to understand about organisms? Circle the **two** correct answers below.

their ecological relationships

whether we can eat them

where they live

their evolutionary relationships

d) Explain why it can be difficult to classify living organisms into distinct groups.

....

Q2 All living things are divided into **kingdoms.** Members of the **plant kingdom** can all make their **own food** using energy from **the Sun.**

a) Give **one other** characteristic of members of the **plant kingdom.**

....

b) Give **two** characteristics of members of the **animal kingdom.**

....

....

c) How many kingdoms are there in total?

....

More On Classification

Q1 Professor Legge has discovered a new **arthropod**.

a) What is an arthropod? Tick the box next to the correct answer.

A plant that has a backbone. ☐

An invertebrate with an external skeleton. ☐

A vertebrate with wings. ☐

b) The new arthropod has **six legs**, **two antennae** and its body is made up of **three parts**. Professor Legge thinks it is an **arachnid**.

i) Is Professor Legge correct?

....

ii) Explain your answer to part **i).**

....

....

c) Which of the following are features of **myriapods**? Circle the **two** correct answers.

legs branch into two at the ends   have between 20 and 400 hundred legs   have eight legs   bodies are made up of segments

d) i) Apart from arachnids and myriapods, name **one** other group of arthropods.

....

ii) Give **one** characteristic of this group.

....

Q2 The diagram to the right shows an **evolutionary tree**.

What do evolutionary trees show? Tick the box next to the correct answer below.

how similar different species look ☐

how closely related different species are to each other ☐

how energy passes through a food chain ☐

species A   species B

Species

Q1　**Species** are named using the **binomial system**.

a)　What is a 'species'? Circle the correct answer below.

> A group of organisms which live in the same area

> A group of organisms which can interbreed to produce fertile offspring

> A group of organisms that look similar

b)　The binomial name for humans is *Homo sapiens*.
　　　Which part of the name refers to the species that humans belong to?

　　　...

Q2　Write the letter '**T**' or '**F**' in each box to show whether the sentences below are **true** (T) or **false** (F).

a)　Similar species tend to live in similar types of habitats.　☐

b)　Species that are not closely related share a recent common ancestor.　☐

c)　Organisms of the same species all look exactly the same.　☐

d)　Organisms of different species have more features in common with each other than with organisms of the same species.　☐

Q3　**Llamas** and **camels** are closely related, but they look very different. Explain why this might be the case.

camel

llama

　　　...

　　　...

　　　...

Top Tips:　Biologists talk about species all the time — so it's definitely worth making sure you know exactly what a species is before you go any further. It'll also help no end when it comes to the exam. Trust me — it's just the sort of thing they like to set you questions on.

Module B2 — Understanding Our Environment

Food Chains and Food Webs

Q1 Nirav is studying a **food chain** on the beach. Nirav's sketch of the food chain is shown below. It has **three trophic levels**.

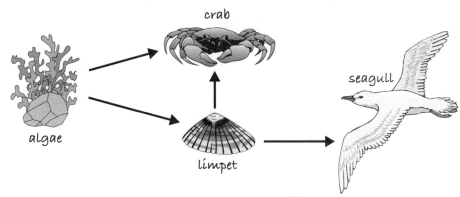

a) What is a 'trophic level'?

....

....

b) i) Which organism in Nirav's food chain is the **producer**?

....

ii) What does the term 'producer' mean?

....

c) i) Tick the correct columns to show which of the organisms in Nirav's food chain are **primary consumers** and which are **secondary consumers**.
For each organism you might have to tick **one** column, **both** or **neither**.
One row has been done for you.

	Primary Consumer	Secondary Consumer
Algae		
Crab		
Limpet	✔	
Seagull		

ii) Suggest a benefit of being **both** a **primary** and a **secondary consumer**.

....

....

Food Chains and Food Webs

Q2   The diagram below shows a **woodland food web**. Last year a chemical was spilt in the woods which was poisonous to voles. The number of **voles decreased significantly**.

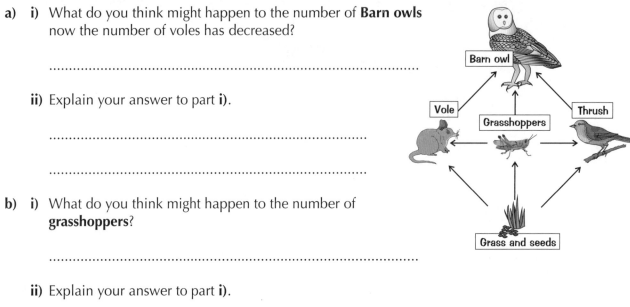

a)   **i)**   What do you think might happen to the number of **Barn owls** now the number of voles has decreased?

....

ii)   Explain your answer to part **i)**.

....

....

b)   **i)**   What do you think might happen to the number of **grasshoppers**?

....

ii)   Explain your answer to part **i)**.

....

Q3   The diagram shows part of a food web in the USA. The **flowerhead weevil** was introduced by **farmers** to eat the musk thistle (a weed).

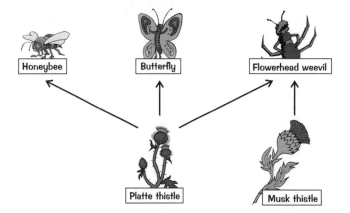

a)   Why might the introduction of the flowerhead weevil **decrease** the number of **platte thistles**?

....

b)   **i)**   What effect will a decrease in the number of platte thistles have on the amount of **wild honey** produced in the area?

Hint: The wild honey is made by the honeybees.

....

ii)   Give a reason for your answer to part **i)**.

....

Pyramids of Biomass and Numbers

Q1 The following diagram shows a garden food chain. The **number** and **dry biomass** of the organisms at each stage in the food chain is shown below.

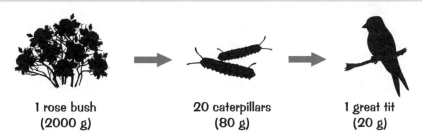

1 rose bush
(2000 g)

20 caterpillars
(80 g)

1 great tit
(20 g)

a) Draw and label a **pyramid of biomass** for the food chain in the grid below. The **top** layer of the pyramid has been drawn for you.

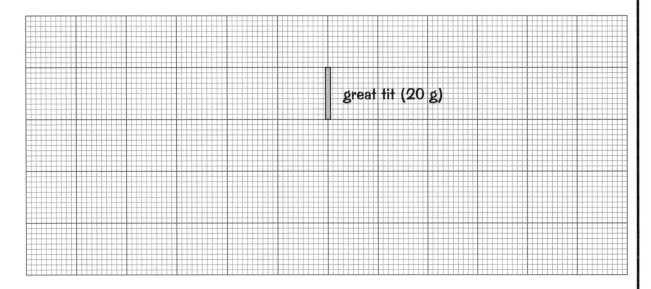

great tit (20 g)

b) Look at the following diagrams.

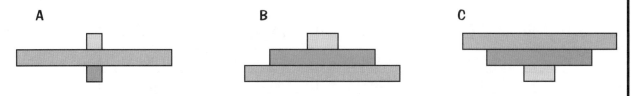

A   B   C

i) Which diagram is most likely to show a **pyramid of numbers** for the food chain above?

Write the correct letter in the space provided. ....

ii) Explain why the pyramid of numbers would be this shape.

pyramid of Egypt

....

....

....

Energy Transfer and Energy Flow

Q1   Complete the sentences below by circling the correct word in each pair.

a)   Nearly all life on Earth depends on **food** / **energy** from the Sun.

b)   **Plants** / **Animals** can make their own food by a process called photosynthesis.

c)   All of the other organisms in a food chain rely on plants for **energy** / **water**.

d)   To obtain energy, animals must **decay** / **eat** plant material or other animals.

e)   Uneaten parts of organisms can become **start** / **end** points for other food chains.

f)   Some of the energy in a food chain is **gained** / **lost** as **growth** / **heat** at each trophic level.

Q2   A **food chain** is shown in the diagram.

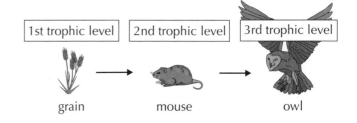

| 1st trophic level | 2nd trophic level | 3rd trophic level |

a)   Put the following amounts of energy under the correct organisms.

500 kJ,   50 000 kJ,   8000 kJ

grain   mouse   owl
....

b)   Calculate the amount of energy lost between the:

i) 1st and 2nd trophic levels. ....

ii) 2nd and 3rd trophic levels. ....

Q3   Another **food chain** is shown below.

leaf it out

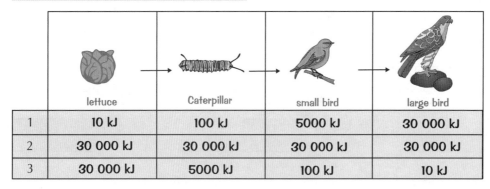

	lettuce	Caterpillar	small bird	large bird
1	10 kJ	100 kJ	5000 kJ	30 000 kJ
2	30 000 kJ	30 000 kJ	30 000 kJ	30 000 kJ
3	30 000 kJ	5000 kJ	100 kJ	10 kJ

a)   Which row, 1, 2 or 3, shows the amount of energy available at each trophic level? ....

b)   Circle the answer below that shows how much energy is lost from the **lettuce** to the **caterpillar**.

| 5000 kJ | | 25 000 kJ | | 30 000 kJ |

c)   Circle the answer below that shows how much energy is lost from the **caterpillar** to the **small bird**.

| 100 kJ | | 4900 kJ | | 5000 kJ |

d)   Give three ways in which energy is lost at each trophic level.

1. ....   2. ....   3. ....

Module B2 — Understanding Our Environment

Interactions Between Organisms

Q1   Some organisms, such as **parasites**, depend entirely on other species for their survival.

a)   Draw lines to match up the beginning of the sentence to its end.

In a parasitic relationship...	both organisms benefit.
In a mutualistic relationship...	an organism lives off a host, but gives nothing back.

b)   **Two** of the organisms below are **parasites**. Circle the correct two.

Flea   Tapeworm   Tiddles   Bumble bee

c)   Describe one example of **mutualism**.

....

....

Q2   Animals and plants **compete** for resources.

a)   Give two reasons why organisms compete for resources.

1. ....

2. ....

b)   Explain why similar animals in the same habitat will be in close competition.

....

c)   Red and grey squirrels compete for food and shelter. The grey squirrel is a stronger competitor than the red squirrel. Suggest how lots of competition from grey squirrels might affect:

i)   the **population size** of the red squirrels.

....

ii)   the **distribution** of the red squirrels.

....

....

Predators, Prey and Adaptation

Q1 Look at the **population graph** for the heron and frog.

a) Which animal is the **predator** and which is the **prey**?

Predator: ....

Prey: ....

b) Shortly after an increase in the number of herons, what happens to the number of frogs?

....

c) If the frogs run out of food, what will happen to the number of herons? Explain your answer.

....

....

Q2 The picture shows a **predator** chasing its **prey**.

a) i) Explain how having **binocular vision** helps **predators** to hunt their prey.

....

ii) Give **one** other adaptation of a predator that helps it to hunt its prey.

....

....

b) i) Some **prey** species have **cryptic colouring**.
How does this adaptation help prey to avoid predators?

....

ii) Give **one** other adaptation of a prey species that helps it to avoid being caught by predators.

....

....

Adaptations to Hot and Cold Environments

Q1 Animals and plants are **adapted** to their habitats.

Explain why animals and plants need to adapt to their habitat.

....

....

Q2 Complete the sentences below about **adaptations to hot environments** by circling the correct word(s) from each pair.

a) To keep cool in warm environments, organisms need to **increase / reduce** heat loss.

b) Being awake at night is **a behavioural / an anatomical** adaptation to living in a hot climate.

c) **Spending the day in the shade / Having large ears** is an anatomical adaptation to hot climates.

d) Having a **small / large** surface area compared to its weight helps an animal to lose heat to its surroundings.

Q3 **Fur seals** are adapted to survive in **very cold places**.

a) Apart from having a thick furry coat, suggest **one** other anatomical adaptation that reduces heat loss.

....

b) i) Fur seals have a **large size** and **small ears**. Does this give them a small or a large **surface area compared to their weight**? Tick the box next to the correct answer below.

small surface area compared to weight [ ]   large surface area compared to weight [ ]

ii) Explain how your answer to part **i)** is an adaptation to the cold.

....

Q4 **Hibernation** is a behavioural adaptation to **cold environments**. Explain how hibernation helps animals in cold environments to **survive**.

....

....

....

Adaptations to Dry Environments

Q1   Margaret's uncle has been on holiday in a **desert** where he took these pictures of **cacti**.
When Margaret asks her uncle why they look so strange he gives her the following passage.

The cactus is an unusual plant. It has a rounded shape
and thick waxy layer called a cuticle. Unlike most
plants it doesn't have leaves — it has spines instead.
Plants need water to survive, but cacti are found
in some of the driest places on Earth.

a) **i)** Use the passage above to suggest **one** adaptation of cacti to dry environments.

....

ii) Suggest how the adaptation you gave in part **i)** helps cacti to survive in dry environments.

....

....

b) **i)** Apart from the ones in the passage, give one other adaptation of plants to dry environments.

....

ii) Explain how this adaptation helps plants to survive.

....

Q2   **Desert animals** are well adapted to living in **dry conditions**.

a) Give **one** adaptation that helps animals to survive in dry environments.

....

b) Explain how your answer to part **a)** helps animals to survive.

....

....

Top Tips: Anything that makes an organism better suited to survive in its habitat is an
adaptation. Adaptations aren't just limited to animals and plants either — things like fungi and bacteria
are also adapted to help them survive. Keep going with these questions — they're good for you.

The Theory of Evolution

Q1   Fill in the gaps in the paragraph using the words provided.

fittest	adapted	common	survive	evolve	resources	natural	genes

Some individuals are better .... to competing for limited

.... than others. These individuals are more likely to

.... It's an idea called the 'survival of the ....'.

Organisms that survive are more likely to reproduce and pass on the ....

that control their successful adaptations to their offspring. The useful adaptations will become

more .... in the population and the species will ....

This is part of Charles Darwin's theory of evolution by .... selection.

Q2   When Darwin first published his work, lots of people didn't agree with his ideas.

a)   Which group of people were particularly upset about Darwin's theory of natural selection?

....

b)   Suggest why these people were upset about Darwin's theory.

....

....

Q3   Giraffes used to have much **shorter** necks than they do today.

The statements below give a possible explanation of how their neck length changed, according to
Darwin's theory. Write numbers in the boxes to show the **order** the statements should be in.
The first and last ones have been done for you.

☐ The giraffes competed for food from low branches. This food started
to become scarce. Many giraffes died before they could breed.

☐ More long-necked giraffes survived to breed, so more giraffes were born with long necks.

☐ A giraffe was born with a longer neck than normal.
The long-necked giraffe was able to eat more food.

[1] All giraffes had short necks.

☐ The long-necked giraffe survived to have lots of
offspring that all had longer necks.

[6] All giraffes have long necks.

The Theory of Evolution

Q4   Marco is researching how groups of organisms change over time.
Complete the passage below by circling the **correct word** from each pair.

Over **long / short** periods of time, groups of organisms can gradually change.

This process is known as **genetics / evolution**. If the conditions in an environment

change, **some / all** species will be able to survive

and some will **evolve / spread out** to cope.

Many species will become **extinct / dinosaurs**.

Q5   Tick the boxes next to the statements which are **true**.

1.   The only theory that explains how evolution happens is Darwin's.   ☐

2.   Other theories to explain how evolution happens have been put forward,   ☐
but Darwin's is still the most widely accepted.

3.   No one else has bothered to test Darwin's theory.   ☐

4.   Darwin's theory has been tested by lots of other scientists.   ☐

Q6   Study the two rabbits shown.

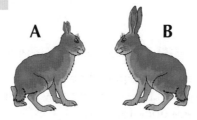

A   **B**

a)   Identify one characteristic that is different between the two rabbits.

....

b)   Suggest which rabbit is more likely to survive and breed. Explain your answer.

....

....

....

c)   Suggest how this characteristic could be passed on to the next generation.

....

The Carbon Cycle

Q1 Follow the instructions below to complete the diagram of part of the **carbon cycle**.

a) Add an arrow or arrows labelled **P** to represent **photosynthesis**.

b) Add an arrow or arrows labelled **R** to represent **respiration**.

c) Add an arrow or arrows labelled **F** to represent **feeding**.

| CO_2 in the air |

| plant | | animal |

Q2 **Living things** and the **air** are both involved in the carbon cycle.

a) Number the sentences below to show how carbon moves from the air to living things.

☐ Animals eat the plants.

☐ Carbon is contained in the air as carbon dioxide.

☐ Plants and animals die.

☐ Plants take in carbon dioxide for photosynthesis and use the carbon to make plant material.

b) Add a fifth point to complete the cycle and explain how carbon in dead organisms is returned to the air.

Point 5: ....

....

Q3 a) Complete the following sentence by circling the correct word from each pair.

Carbon is an important **element** / **compound** that is constantly being **used up** / **recycled**.

b) What is the one way that carbon is removed from the atmosphere?

....

c) In what form is carbon removed from the atmosphere?

....

d) How is this carbon passed on through the food chain?

....

....

e) By what process do **all** living organisms release carbon into the air?

....

Module B2 — Understanding Our Environment

The Carbon Cycle

Q4   Samantha's dog tore up her biology homework. She's trying to piece it back together, but some of the words are missing. Complete the passage using all of the words provided.

carbon dioxide	recycled	decomposers	fungi	decay

All plants and animals eventually die and .... When they

decay, they are broken down by organisms called ....

These organisms are things like .... and bacteria in the soil.

They release .... back into the atmosphere as they break

material down. This allows carbon to be ...., so it can be

used again by living organisms.

Q5   The diagram below shows a version of the **carbon cycle**.

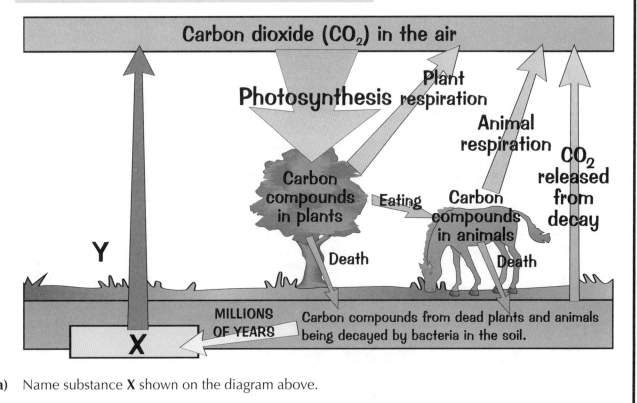

a)   Name substance **X** shown on the diagram above.

....

b)   Name the process labelled **Y** on the diagram above.

....

Top Tips: Knowing the processes in the carbon cycle is really important. The best way to learn them is to get stuck in and work your way around the cycle. The more times you go over it, the less scary it will seem — and the easier you'll find the carbon cycle questions in the exam.

The Nitrogen Cycle and Decomposition

Q1 Tick the correct boxes to show whether each of the sentences below is **true** (T) or **false** (F).

a) Nitrogen is an **element**. ☐ T ☐ F

b) Nitrogen is needed for **growth**. ☐ T ☐ F

c) Air is **21%** nitrogen. ☐ T ☐ F

d) The nitrogen found in the air is **a reactive gas**. ☐ T ☐ F

Q2 The diagram below shows the nitrogen cycle.

Nitrogen in the atmosphere

A

B

Decomposition

Nitrates in the soil

Nitrates absorbed by roots

a) Underline the name of the process labelled **A** in the list below.

decomposition   photosynthesis   eating   respiration

b) What do plants make from **nitrates**? Underline the correct answer below.

fats   carbohydrates   proteins   sugar

c) i) Name the process labelled **B** on the diagram.

....

ii) What type of organisms are responsible for process **B** on the diagram?

....

Q3 Explain why nitrogen takes **longer** to be recycled in very **acidic** soils than in neutral soils.

....

....

Human Impact on the Environment

Q1 Humans are having an **increasing impact** on their environment.
One reason for this is that the world **population** is growing.

a) A growing population means that more **finite resources** are being used.
Give two examples of finite resources.

1. ....   2. ....

b) Name two **pollutants** that will increase as the human population grows.

1. ....   2. ....

Q2 Look at the list of **pollutants** on the right.   **Carbon dioxide**   **CFCs**   **Sulfur dioxide**

a) Which of the pollutants in the list is breaking down **ozone** in the atmosphere?

....

b) i) Which of the pollutants in the list is contributing to **global warming**?

....

ii) Suggest **one** problem that global warming might cause.

....

Q3 The graph below shows the amount of **sulfur dioxide** released in the UK between 1970 and 2003.

a) What releases pollutants like **sulfur dioxide** into the atmosphere?

....

b) In which year shown on the graph were sulfur dioxide emissions highest? ....

c) Approximately how much sulfur dioxide was emitted in 2000? ....

d) Give one **problem** caused by sulfur dioxide in the atmosphere.

....

Human Impact on the Environment

Q4 Lichens are often studied to find out how much **air pollution** there is in an area.

a) Write the letter 'T' or 'F' in the box to show whether the statement below is true (T) or false (F). ☐

Pollution can affect the number and type of organisms that can survive in a particular place.

b) What do we call an organism whose presence can give us information about pollution in an area?

....

c) The graph shows the number of lichens found in different areas.

Use the graph to help you decide if a high number of lichens indicates a badly polluted atmosphere or a clean atmosphere. Explain your answer.

....

....

....

d) Name one organism you could look for in a river to find out how polluted it is.

....

Q5 Phosphorus is a fertiliser that can pollute lakes and streams. Dave is investigating the local water quality. He collects data on the **phosphorus concentration** in the water at different sites along a nearby river. His data is shown in the table below.

Site	phosphorus concentration (milligrams/m^3)
1	52.8
2	76.2
3	93.5

a) At which site is the phosphorus concentration the **highest**?

....

b) Has Dave measured the pollution level **directly** or used an **indicator species**?

....

c) Explain your answer to part **b)**.

....

....

Endangered Species

Q1 Fill in the gaps in the passage, using words from the list below.

future	endangered	plants	conservation	extinct

.... programmes often help humans as well as .... species.

One example is the conservation of rainforests. Many of the medicines that we

use today come from .... If the rainforests are not protected, species that

haven't been discovered yet may become .... This could mean that we

miss out on useful medicines in the ....

Q2 The mountain gorilla is an **endangered** species threatened with **extinction**.
One reason for this is that its forest habitat is being destroyed.

a) Apart from habitat destruction, give **two** reasons why species become endangered.

....

....

You don't need to know specifically about gorillas — think about how animals in general become extinct.

b) How could a reduction in the **number of individuals** cause gorillas to become **extinct**?

....

....

Q3 It is our responsibility to protect the future of **endangered species**.

a) How can **education programmes** from organisations like Greenpeace and the RSPB protect endangered species?

....

b) Give **one** way that endangered species can be **legally protected**.

....

c) What is an **artificial ecosystem**?

....

d) How can **captive breeding programmes** help to protect endangered species?

....

e) Explain how **seed banks** can help to protect endangered plant species.

....

Sustainable Development

Q1 Tick the box next to the best definition for the term **sustainable development**.

'Doing whatever it takes to protect the environment, even if today's population suffers.' ☐

'Providing for the needs of today's increasing population by using up natural resources.' ☐

'Providing for the needs of today's increasing population without harming the environment.' ☐

Q2 Tick the right boxes to say whether the sentences below are **true** or **false**.

		True	False
a)	Sustainable resources will run out.	☐	☐
b)	Some whale species are endangered.	☐	☐
c)	Whales still have commercial value when they are dead.	☐	☐
d)	The cosmetics industry has not contributed to the endangerment of whales.	☐	☐
e)	Captive breeding can help endangered whales.	☐	☐
f)	Keeping whales in captivity is not useful for scientists.	☐	☐

Q3 Many people think **sustainable development** might help to solve environmental problems.

Describe how the following resources can be maintained in a **sustainable** way:

a) Fish stocks.

....

....

b) Woodland.

....

....

Q4 Explain the role that **education** can play in sustainable development.

....

....

....

Top Tips: Now that you've given the whole section a go, it's time for you to take on the mixed questions. I know it's boring and tricky, but sitting down and doing these questions is the best possible way to prepare yourself for those pesky GCSEs. Take a deep breath and turn over the page...

Mixed Questions — Module B2

Q1 Two types of **goose** found in the UK are the greylag goose and the white-fronted goose. The Latin name for the greylag goose is *Anser anser* and the white-fronted goose is *Anser albifrons*.

a) What name is given to the system of identifying species by giving them two names? Circle the correct answer below.

| the dinomial system | the binomial system | the binaming system |

b) Explain why this system is used all over the world for naming species.

....

....

....

Q2 **Environmental pollution** is a big problem in some areas.

a) i) Magnus suspects that a paper factory down the road from his house is **polluting** a local river. Which of the following species would allow Magnus to tell whether the river is polluted? Tick the boxes next to the correct answers.

water lice ☐   sludgeworms ☐

lichens ☐   mayfly larvae ☐

whales ☐   rat-tailed maggots ☐

ii) Suggest what the paper factory in Magnus's town might do to make the business more **sustainable**.

Hint: you need trees to make paper.

....

....

b) Environmental pollution is being made worse by the **rising human population**. Circle the correct word in each pair to complete the following passage.

The world's human population is increasing **exponentially / excitedly**.

This is because the birth rate is **lower / higher** than the death rate.

More people means that **more / fewer** resources are being used.

This creates more pollution.

Mixed Questions — Module B2

Q3   **Acid rain** is a big problem associated with the burning of fossil fuels.

a) Name one pollutant that causes acid rain.

....

b) Suggest **two** problems that are caused by acid rain.

....

c) The presence of some fish species can show whether a lake has been polluted by acid rain. What name is given to species that can be used to show pollution?

....

Q4   Lots of plants are **pollinated** by **insects**.

a) Is this an example of a **mutualistic** or a **parasitic** relationship?

....

b) Explain your answer to part **a)**.

....

....

Q5   The graph shows how the **populations** of snowy owls (predators) and lemmings (their prey) vary in a community over time.

a) Just after the population of lemmings increases, the population of snowy owls increases. Explain why this happens.

....

....

b) Give one **adaptation** that snowy owls might have that make them good predators.

....

c) Most owls today have excellent night vision. Circle the correct word(s) from each pair to complete the sentences below and explain how owls might have **evolved** to have this characteristic.

> Some owls had genes that gave them good night vision. This allowed them to hunt
>
> for prey at night. These owls were **less / more** likely to survive, reproduce and
>
> **pass on / evolve** the genes that give them good night vision. These genes have become
>
> **less / more** common in the owl population, so that most owls now have night vision.

The Earth's Structure

Q1 Use the words below to **label** the diagram of the inside of the Earth.

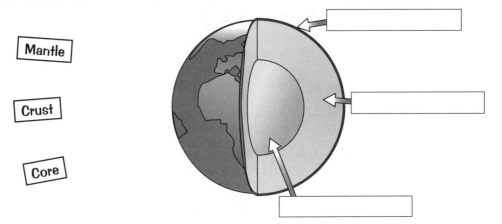

Mantle

Crust

Core

Q2 Draw a line to match up each key phrase or word to the correct description.

Crust   Shock waves produced by an earthquake or an explosion.

Mantle   Large pieces of the lithosphere.

Tectonic Plates   A solid section of the Earth between the crust and the core.

Seismic waves   The Earth's thin outer layer of solid rock.

Q3 The layers of the Earth contain different materials and have different **properties**.

a) i) What parts of the Earth make up the lithosphere?

....

ii) Describe what the lithosphere is like.

....

b) Which **metal** is thought to make up the Earth's **core**?

....

Q4 Complete the sentences below by circling the correct option from each pair.

a) The Earth's crust is so **hot** / **thick** that you can't drill through it to study the Earth's inner structure.

b) Instead, geologists use **seismic** / **electromagnetic** waves.

c) Seismic waves can be produced by **earthquakes** / **floods**.

d) By measuring where the waves are detected scientists can work out the **shape** / **structure** of the Earth.

Plate Tectonics

Q1   Look at the diagram showing the boundary between two **tectonic plates**.

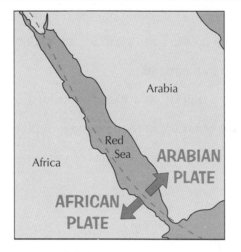

china plate

The Red Sea is widening at a speed of 1.6 cm per year.

a)   If the sea level stays the same, how much will the Red Sea widen in **10 000 years**?
Give your answer in **cm**.

....

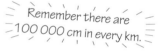

Remember there are 100 000 cm in every km.

b)   Give your answer to part **a)** in **km**.

....

c)   Today, the Red Sea is exactly 325 km wide at a certain point.
How wide will the Red Sea be at this point in **10 000** years' time?

....

....

Q2   The map below on the left shows where most of the world's earthquakes take place.

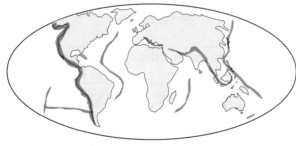

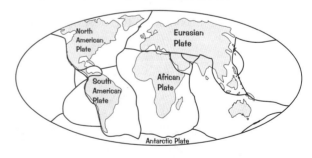

= main earthquake zones

Compare this map to the one on the right showing the tectonic plates.
What do you notice about the main earthquake zones?

....

....

Plate Tectonics

Q3 The Earth's surface is made up of large plates of rock.

Tick the boxes to say whether the following statements are **true** or **false**.

	True	False
a) The plates of rock that make up the Earth's surface are called techno plates.	☐	☐
b) The plates are less dense than the mantle.	☐	☐
c) The plates of rock move very quickly, at a speed of about 2.5 cm per second.	☐	☐
d) Volcanoes and earthquakes often occur in the middle of plates.	☐	☐
e) The Earth's surface looked very different millions of years ago.	☐	☐

Q4 The sentences below all contain **one** mistake. Write a correct version of each sentence.

a) A theory is an idea used to prove something.

....

b) Earth scientists don't accept the theory of plate tectonics.

....

c) Before plate tectonics there were no other theories to explain the Earth's surface.

....

d) The theory of plate tectonics has been discussed and tested by a small group of scientists.

....

Q5 Many scientists think that sea floor spreading is good **evidence** for plate tectonics.

a) Tick the box next to the description that best explains the diagram of sea floor spreading.

☐ The magma rises up through a break in the crust and hardens to form new crust.

☐ Plates on the ocean floor move together, squeezing magma out of the mantle.

☐ The weight of the ocean pushes magma back down into the mantle.

b) Why does sea floor spreading provide evidence for plate tectonics?

....

Volcanic Eruptions

Q1   Magma and lava are both **molten rock**.

a)   What is the difference between magma and lava?

....

....

b)   Volcanoes can erupt different types of lava.
Circle the two words that best describe the different types of lava.

Solid   Cold   Runny

Thick   Squidgy   Hard

Q2   Igneous rocks are formed from molten rock.

a)   Tick the box next to the sentence that best describes how igneous rocks are formed.

Molten rock is pressed under layers of solid rock.   ☐

Molten rock cools down and becomes solid.   ☐

Molten rock is pushed back into the crust and solidifies.   ☐

b)   Explain why some igneous rocks contain small crystals and some contain large crystals.

....

....

Q3   Volcanoes are formed when molten rock from the mantle breaks through the Earth's crust.

a)   Complete the sentences below by circling the correct word from each pair.

i)   Scientists study eruptions to learn more about the **structure** / **climate** of the Earth.

ii)   Volcanoes that produce **thick** / **runny** lava often erupt explosively.

iii)   People live near volcanoes because volcanic soil is great for **building on** / **farming**.

b)   Which of the following statements about volcanic eruptions is true? Circle the correct answer.

A — Geologists don't study volcanoes to try and predict eruptions — they will always be impossible to predict.

B — Geologists study volcanoes to try to predict how likely they are to erupt in the future.

Top Tips: There are no end of problems with predicting volcanic eruptions. There are likely to be loads of people living near a volcano — it'd be impossible to evacuate them all every time scientists thought there might possibly be an eruption some time soon. It just wouldn't work.

Limestone and Marble

Q1   Limestone and marble are both made from the **same** chemical compound.

a) Give the **chemical name** of this compound.

....

b) Limestone can **thermally decompose**.

i) Explain what thermal decomposition means.

....

....

ii) Write out the **word equation** for the thermal decomposition of calcium carbonate.

....

iii) Complete the **symbol equation** below for the thermal decomposition of calcium carbonate.

$$CaCO_3 \rightarrow \text{.........................} + \text{.........................}$$

c) Limestone, marble and granite are all used to construct buildings.
Arrange these three rocks in order of **hardness**.

marble   limestone   granite

Increasing hardness

....

Q2   Thermal decomposition is an important chemical reaction. Tick the box next to the equations which show thermal decomposition reactions.

a) $CuCO_3 \xrightarrow{heat} CuO + CO_2$ ☐

b) $Mg + Cl_2 \rightarrow MgCl_2$ ☐

c) $CH_4 + 2O_2 \xrightarrow{heat} CO_2 + 2H_2O$ ☐

Remember what thermal decomposition is and don't forget to look at the numbers of atoms on each side of the equation.

d) $2Zn(NO_3)_2 \xrightarrow{heat} 2ZnO + 4NO_2 + O_2$ ☐

Top Tips: Even though limestone and marble are both made from the same stuff, they don't have the same properties because they're made in **different** ways. It's just like when you bake a cake — if you have the oven too high you'll create a blackened mess. It's still made of the same stuff as a cake but it won't taste as good, not like those ones Mamma used to make...

Construction Materials

Q1 Match each **construction material** to the **raw materials** that are needed to make it.

CONSTRUCTION MATERIALS

cement

bricks

iron

aluminium

glass

RAW MATERIALS

ores

limestone

clay

sand

Some construction materials are made from more than one raw material from the list.

Q2 Quarrying limestone can cause lots of **problems**.

Circle **three environmental** problems quarrying can cause.

Increased noise

Produces dust

Creates a new habitat for wildlife

More tourists

Damage to landscape

Creates more jobs

Costs money to fill in the quarry

Q3 Choose from the words below to complete the paragraphs.

clay	quick	gravel	cheap
heating	sand	calcium carbonate	water

a) Cement is made by .... limestone (..),

and .... together.

b) The cement can be made into concrete by mixing it with ....,

aggregates (.................................) and .... and leaving it to set.

c) Concrete is a very .... and .... way of making buildings.

Q4 Many buildings are made from '**reinforced concrete**'.

a) Describe how concrete can be reinforced.

....

b) Complete the sentence by circling the correct word.

Reinforced concrete is called a **compound** / **composite** material.

Extracting Pure Copper

Q1   Copper is found in the ground in **ores**.

a)   Suggest how copper could be **extracted** from the ore. Circle the correct answer.

Heat with carbon   Cool to below its   Mix with pure copper
                          freezing point   and leave overnight

b)   Circle the process that's often used to **purify** the extracted copper.

Evaporation   Filtration   Electrolysis

Q2   The apparatus shown below could be used to **purify copper**.
Label the diagram using the words below.

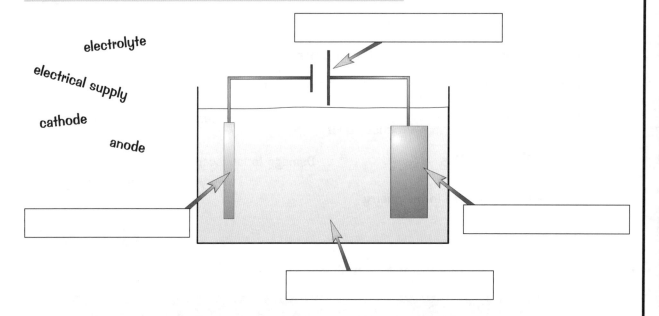

electrolyte

electrical supply

cathode

anode

Q3   Complete the sentence about **reduction** by circling the correct word.

A reduction reaction is one where a molecule **gains** / **loses** oxygen.

Q4   **Recycling** copper has advantages and disadvantages.

a)   Tick the boxes to show which of the following are **good reasons** for recycling copper.

☐   It's cheaper than mining new copper.

☐   It uses less energy and therefore less fossil fuel.

☐   You obtain a higher quality of copper.

☐   We can use less copper to make products.

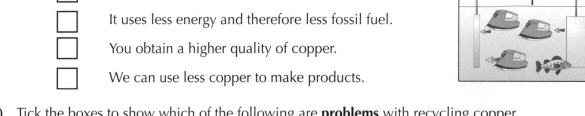

b)   Tick the boxes to show which of the following are **problems** with recycling copper.

☐   It's hard to convince people it's worth the effort.

☐   Sorting the copper takes time and energy.

☐   Most of the copper you get at the end can't be used again.

Alloys

Q1 Choose from the words below to complete the paragraph.

carbon	non-metal	alloy	brass

If you mix a metal with another element you get an ....

The other element may be a .... For example, steel is made

when iron is mixed with small amounts of .... The other

element could also be another metal. For example, ... is a

mixture of copper and zinc.

Q2 Metals are mixed with other elements to give them different properties for different uses.

a) Tick the correct boxes to show whether each statement is **true** or **false**.

                                     True False

i) Steel contains copper. ☐ ☐

ii) Amalgam contains mercury. ☐ ☐

iii) Brass contains zinc. ☐ ☐

iv) Solder contains aluminium. ☐ ☐

v) Brass contains carbon. ☐ ☐

b) Draw lines to join up the following alloys with their uses.
Some alloys will have more than one use.

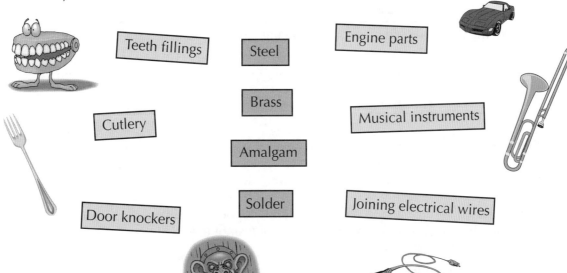

Teeth fillings   Steel   Engine parts

Brass   Musical instruments

Cutlery

Amalgam

Door knockers   Solder   Joining electrical wires

Alloys

Q3   The table below shows three types of **bronze** alloy. These alloys **only** contain tin and copper.

a)   What is the % of copper in **commercial bronze**?

....

b)   What type of bronze do you think is most likely to be used for gold decorations?

....

Alloy	% tin	% copper	Appearance
Hi-Tin Bronze	20	80	Silver
Commercial bronze	10		Dark orange
Hi-copper bronze	5	95	Gold

Q4   Alloys have different **properties** than the metals they were made from.

a)   Steel is used to make drill bits. Circle the **two** properties of steel that are most useful in drills.

hard   **strong**   **resistant to corrosion**

Corrosion is when metals are destroyed slowly by a chemical reaction.

b)   Steel is also used to make ships. Circle **one** property of steel that makes it more useful than iron in ships.

hard   **strong**   **resistant to corrosion**

Q5   The table below shows some properties of five metals.

The higher the number the better the metal conducts electricity.

	Electrical conductivity	Density (g/cm³)	Hardness (resistance to scratching)
Aluminium	50	2.7	2.75
Copper	90	8.9	3.0
Gold	65	19.3	2.5
Iron	18	7.9	4.0
Zinc	28	7.1	2.5

The higher the number, the harder the metal.

a)   Which of the metals would be good for making electrical wires? Explain your answer.

....

....

b)   Aluminium is used to make aeroplanes. Suggest why it is a good material for this.

....

c)   Most gold used for jewellery is an alloy of gold, copper and silver.
Apart from the price, why do you think pure gold is not used?

....

Top Tips: The properties of an alloy determine what it's used for, e.g. if you want an alloy that's strong, but lightweight and will harden over time, then a great solution is duralumin, which is aluminium with some copper, manganese and magnesium added to it.

Iron and Aluminium

Q1   Use the words below to complete the paragraph.

oxide	salty	iron	oxidation	rusting	water

.... is the corrosion of .... If iron comes into

contact with both oxygen and ...., a chemical reaction happens.

This is known as an .... reaction, and it forms an ....

This reaction is speeded up if the water is acidic or ....

Q2   The table below shows some **properties** of metals. Tick or cross the boxes next to iron and aluminium to show whether they **do** or **don't** have each property.

Malleable means easy to hammer into shape.

Property	Iron	Aluminium
Magnetic		
Easily corrodes		
Good electrical conductor		
Malleable		

Q3   Terry is studying the **corrosion** of different metals. She puts pieces of **iron** and **aluminium** in three different beakers for **one week**. Her results are shown below.

	Iron	Aluminium
Beaker of salty water	The iron rusted a lot	Nothing happened
Empty beaker	Some rust appeared on the surface	Nothing happened
Beaker of dilute sulfuric acid	The iron rusted a lot	Nothing happened

a)   Describe what the experiment tells Terry about the corrosion of:

i) iron. ....

ii) aluminium. ....

b)   Explain why nothing happened to the aluminium.

....

....

....

c)   Give the **word equation** for the reaction that happened to the iron.

....

Building Cars

Q1 Steel and aluminium are both used for building **car bodies**.
Match up the metals with their correct **properties**.

Doesn't corrode easily

Strong

Aluminium

Steel

Low density

Cheap

You can use each property once, twice or not at all.

Q2 Fill in the labels on the diagram to show which **material** is used to make each part of the car and the **advantage** of that material.

Materials:
Plastic
Copper
Glass
Fibres

Advantages:
Light and hardwearing
Electrical conductor
Transparent
Long lasting

Dashboard
Material:
Advantage:

Windows
Material:
Advantage:

Seats
Material:
Advantage:

Electrical wiring
Material:
Advantage:

Q3 There are lots of advantages and disadvantages to **recycling car parts**.

a) Which of the following statements are **true** and which are **false**?

True False

i) Cars are recycled to save natural resources and to reduce landfill use. ☐ ☐

ii) There are no laws stating how much of a new car must be recyclable. ☐ ☐

iii) At the moment it's mostly just the metal from cars that's recycled. ☐ ☐

b) What is the biggest problem with recycling the **non-metal** bits of a car?

....

....

Acids and Bases

Q1   Acids and alkalis can be tested for using indicators.

a)   Complete the following statement about litmus indicator with the correct colours.

Acids turn .... litmus ...., and alkalis turn .... litmus ....

b)   Which ions are always present in an acid? ....

Q2   Place the liquids below into the table to show which are **acids** and which are **alkalis**.
Then circle the liquid that will contain the highest **H⁺ concentration**.

Washing up liquid (pH 8)   Lemonade (pH 3)   Cola (pH 2)

Milk (pH 6)   Vinegar (pH 3)   NaOH solution (pH 13)

Acids	Alkalis

Q3   Acids can be **neutralised** by bases and bases can be **neutralised** by acids.

a)   Which is the correct word equation for a **neutralisation reaction**? Circle your answer.

salt + acid → base + water   acid + base → salt + water   acid + water → base + salt

b)   Complete the following sentences using just **one word** for each.

i)   Solutions which are not acidic or alkaline are said to be ....

ii)   An alkali is a base that is soluble in ....

iii) When a substance is neutral it has a pH of ....

Q4   Draw lines to match the substances below to their **universal indicator colour**,
pH value and **acid/base strength**. One example has been done for you.

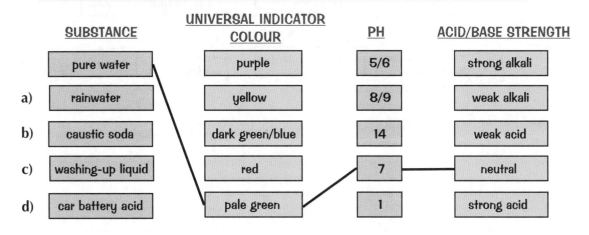

Reactions of Acids

Q1   **Acids** react with **metal oxides** and **metal hydroxides** to form a salt and water.

a) Use the words below each reaction to complete the word equations.

i) hydrochloric acid + lead oxide → .... chloride + water

oxygen   lead   hydrogen

ii) nitric acid + copper hydroxide → copper .... + water

hydride   hydroxide   nitrate

iii) sulfuric acid + zinc oxide → zinc sulfate + ...

oxygen   water   hydrogen

iv) hydrochloric acid + ... oxide → nickel .... + water

nickel   chloride   hydride

b) Fill in the blanks to complete the word equations.

i) nitric acid + copper oxide → .... nitrate + water

ii) phosphoric acid + ... hydroxide → sodium phosphate + water

Q2 a) Put a tick in the box next to any of the sentences below that are **true**.

i) Metal oxides and metal hydroxides neutralise bases. ☐

ii) Acids react with metal oxides to form a salt and water. ☐

iii) Hydrogen gas is formed when an acid reacts with an alkali. ☐

iv) Salts and water are formed when acids react with metal hydroxides. ☐

v) Sodium hydroxide is an acid that dissolves in water. ☐

b) Use the chemicals below to write **word equations** for the following reactions.

water   sodium chloride   hydrochloric acid

sulfuric acid

copper oxide   copper sulfate   water   sodium hydroxide

i) The reaction between hydrochloric acid and sodium hydroxide.

....

ii) The reaction between sulfuric acid and copper oxide.

....

Module C2 — Chemical Resources

Reactions of Acids

Q3 One type of **neutralisation** reaction is the reaction between an **acid** and a **metal oxide**.

a) Complete the general equation for the reaction between a metal oxide and an acid.

ACID + METAL OXIDE → .... + ...

b) Which combination of substances would react in this way?
Choose the correct answer from the options below. Tick **one** box.

Magnesium and sulfuric acid. ☐

Sodium hydroxide and water. ☐

Copper oxide and hydrochloric acid. ☐

Q4 Metal oxides and metal hydroxides are bases. Circle the **bases** in the list of compounds below.

copper sulfate

copper oxide

lead hydroxide

sodium chloride   hydrogen chloride

tin oxide

lead sulfide

potassium hydroxide

carbon dioxide

Q5 **Acids** react with **metal carbonates** in neutralisation reactions.

a) Use the words below each reaction to complete the word equations.

i) phosphoric acid + ... carbonate →

copper .... + water + ...

copper   phosphate   carbon dioxide

ii) .... acid + magnesium .... →

.... nitrate + ... + carbon dioxide

magnesium   nitric   carbonate   water

b) Complete this word equation for the reaction of sulfuric acid with lithium carbonate:

sulfuric acid + lithium carbonate → .... + ...+ ....

Top Tips: Well take my socks off and paint me blue — that's a lot of equations.
But don't forget, if you can remember the different products of neutralisation reactions you can work
'em all out. Just take the name of the metal and add it to the first bit of the acid. The clues are all there...

Fertilisers

Q1 Choose from the words to fill in the blanks below. Use each word only once.

well	yield	growth	phosphorus	essential

Fertilisers are used to increase crop .... They provide plants with

.... elements needed for ...., making crops grow faster and

bigger. These elements include nitrogen, ... and potassium. If plants don't

get enough of these elements, they won't grow ....

Q2 Sophie is concerned about the amount of **fertiliser** that gets washed into **rivers**.

a) Name the essential element(s) in the fertilisers below.

  i) Urea — $(NH_2)_2CO$ Essential element(s): ....

  ii) Potassium nitrate — KNO_3 Essential element(s): ....

  iii) Ammonium phosphate — $(NH_4)_3PO_4$ Essential element(s): ....

b) Circle the part of the plant which absorbs the most minerals.

c) Sophie suggests making the fertilisers into **insoluble** pellets.
Why is this a bad idea?

....

Insoluble means that it won't dissolve.

Q3 There are **advantages** and **disadvantages** to using fertilisers.

a) Give **two** disadvantages of using lots of fertilisers.

1. ....

2. ....

b) Give **one** advantage of using fertilisers.

....

c) Why is ammonia (NH_3) important for food production?

....

Preparing Fertilisers

Q1   Tamsin prepares **ammonium sulfate** in the lab using the apparatus shown in the diagram.

Label the apparatus.

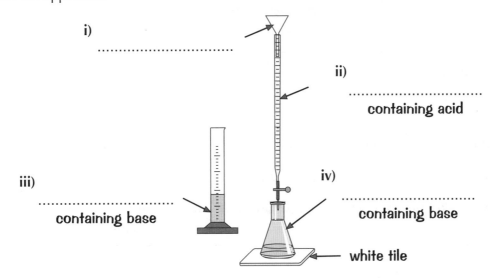

i) ....

ii) ....
containing acid

iii) ....
containing base

iv) ....
containing base

white tile

Q2   Draw lines to join each type of fertiliser to the **acid** and **alkali** that's used to make it.
You may need to use some reactants more than once.

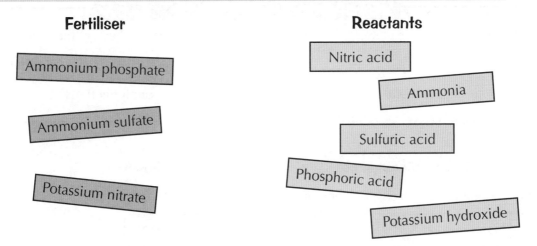

Fertiliser

Ammonium phosphate

Ammonium sulfate

Potassium nitrate

Reactants

Nitric acid

Ammonia

Sulfuric acid

Phosphoric acid

Potassium hydroxide

Q3   **Ammonium nitrate** is often used as a fertiliser.

a)   Name the acid and the base used to make ammonium nitrate.

acid: ....

base: ....

b)   Name the essential element that ammonium nitrate provides to plants.

....

The Haber Process

Q1   The Haber process is used to make **ammonia** (NH_3).

a)   The equation for the reaction is:

> nitrogen + hydrogen $\rightleftharpoons$ ammonia

i) Write the balanced symbol equation for this reaction.

....

ii) What does the $\rightleftharpoons$ symbol mean? ....

iii) Name the reactants in the forward reaction. ....

b)   Name two **useful substances** that can be made from ammonia.

1. ....

2. ....

Q2   Fill in the blanks in the passage by choosing from the words in the list.

| hydrogen | cracking | air |

Chemical manufacturers need two gases to make ammonia. They get the nitrogen

from the .... The other gas, ..., usually

comes from natural gas or from .... of oil fractions.

Q3   The **industrial conditions** for the Haber process are carefully chosen.

a)   What conditions are used? Tick one box.

☐ high pressure, 450 °C   ☐ low pressure, 1500 °C

☐ high pressure, 200 °C   ☐ low pressure, 450 °C

b)   What catalyst is used? Tick one box.

☐ Nickel   ☐ Iron   ☐ Copper   ☐ Zinc

c)   What happens to the hydrogen and nitrogen that do not react?

....

Top Tips: Changing the conditions in a reversible reaction to get more product sounds great, but don't forget that those conditions might make the reaction too slow to make any money from it.

Minimising the Cost of Production

Q1 Tick the correct boxes to show whether the following sentences about manufacturing chemicals are **true** or **false**.

		True	False
a)	Increasing the temperature **decreases** the energy costs.	☐	☐
b)	Increasing the pressure **increases** the plant cost.	☐	☐
c)	Catalysts **increase** the rate of reaction and **decrease** the running costs.	☐	☐
d)	Making the process more automated **reduces** the number of people needed.	☐	☐
e)	Recycling unreacted raw materials **increases** the production costs.	☐	☐
f)	Involving lots of people in the process **reduces** the production costs.	☐	☐
g)	Using lots of machinery instead of people **decreases** the running costs.	☐	☐

Q2 Join the factors involved in a particular **production process** to the correct **cost**. The first one has been done for you.

hydrogen

Price of Energy

staff pensions

Cost of Starting Materials

electricity

Labour Costs

pipes

Plant Costs

heating

staff wages

high pressure machinery

nitrogen

Q3 A drugs company tests two processes for making a new drug. Rupert records the **production cost** and the total **yield** for each process.

a) Use the graphs to fill in the table below with the **production cost** and **total yield** for processes A and B.

	Process A	Process B
Production Cost (£)		
Total Yield (g)		

b) Suggest why the company decides to use process B, even though it has a higher production cost.

....

Salt

Q1 Tick the boxes to show whether the following statements are **true** or **false**.   True False

a) Salt is only found underground. ☐ ☐

b) There are no deposits of rock salt in Cheshire. ☐ ☐

c) Salt can be mined by pumping hot water underground. ☐ ☐

d) The holes left by mining salt must be filled in, or they could cause subsidence. ☐ ☐

e) Salt is used as a preservative and a flavouring. ☐ ☐

Q2 **Circle** the correct answer for each of the questions below.

a) Chlorine is made by the electrolysis of brine. You can test for chlorine by:

Using a glowing splint — chlorine will relight it.   Using damp litmus paper — chlorine will bleach it.

Using universal indicator — chlorine will turn it purple.

b) Two of the products of the electrolysis of brine are used to make bleach. They are:

Chlorine and hydrogen.   Hydrogen and sodium hydroxide.   Chlorine and sodium hydroxide.

Q3 The diagram shows the **industrial set-up** used to electrolyse concentrated brine.

a) i) State the electrode where hydrogen is formed. ....

ii) State the electrode where chlorine is formed. ....

b) Why are inert electrodes used?

....

....

c) Identify the substances labelled A, B and C on the diagram. Choose from the options in the box below.

| Cl$_2$ | H$_2$ | brine |

A .... B .... C ....

Q4 Salt is a source of **chlorine**, **hydrogen** and **sodium hydroxide**.
Match up these chemicals with the products they are used to make.

margarine   Chlorine   plastics such
                                          as PVC
soap
        Sodium hydroxide
used to
sterilise water   Hydrogen   solvents

Mixed Questions — Module C2

Q1   **Limestone** is a useful construction material.

a)   Limestone is made from **calcium carbonate**.
Circle another building material made from calcium carbonate.

   Sandstone   Granite   Marble   Clay

b)   Circle the correct name below for the type of reaction shown in this equation:

   Calcium carbonate → calcium oxide + carbon dioxide

   neutralisation   combustion   thermal decomposition   electrolysis

c)   Limestone can be used to make other building materials.
Complete the flow diagram to show what other materials can be made from limestone.

Limestone	→ heat with clay →		→ add sand, water and gravel →	

Q2   **Farmers** often apply **fertilisers** to their fields.

a)   Why do farmers find fertilisers useful?

....

b)   Fertilisers applied as solid **pellets** won't work until it **rains**. Explain why.

....

c)   Ammonium nitrate (NH_4NO_3) is a good fertiliser, because it contains two sources of **nitrogen**.
Apart from nitrogen, name **two** other nutrients which are essential for plant growth.

....

d)   Pedro puts large amounts of ammonium nitrate fertiliser on his prize winning vegetables.
The fish in the river running along the bottom of Pedro's veg patch all start to die.
Explain why this could be Pedro's fault.

....

....

....

Top Tips: Fertilisers are always given a lot of bad press but without them there'd be a lot less food to go round. The trick is not to use too much fertiliser — that'll stop those pesky environmental problems.

Mixed Questions — Module C2

Q3   **Copper** is a metal with a variety of uses.

a)   Copper is dug out of the ground as an **ore**. Explain what copper **ore** is.

....

b)   In copper ore the copper is chemically joined to oxygen.

   i)   Explain how you would **remove the oxygen** from the copper.

   ....

   ii)   What **type** of reaction is this? Circle the correct answer.

   oxidation   reduction   neutralisation

c)   Copper is used in **alloys**. Circle the alloys below which contain copper.

   bronze   amalgam   brass   steel   solder

d)   What is purified copper used for in cars? Why is this?

   ....

   ....

e)   Aluminium is also used in cars. Why is aluminium used for parts of a car engine?

   ....

   ....

f)   Suggest **two** advantages of **recycling** the copper and other metals used in cars.

   ....

   ....

Q4   The Earth's surface is split into large rocky **plates**.

a)   What are these plates called? ....

b)   **Volcanoes** can form where plates meet if molten rock breaks through the Earth's crust.
     Is the type of rock formed from volcanoes metamorphic, sedimentary or igneous?

   ....

c)   Which rock, A or B, is more likely to have
     formed by cooling **quickly** above ground?
     Circle the correct slice of rock.

   Slice of
   rock A

   Slice of
   rock B

Mixed Questions — Module C2

Q5   Chlorine, hydrogen and sodium hydroxide are produced by **electrolysing brine**.

a)   Place each of the uses listed below into the correct box to show whether it is a use of chlorine, hydrogen or sodium hydroxide. Some uses may belong in more than one box.

PVC   soap   solvents   margarine   disinfecting water   bleach

CHLORINE
HYDROGEN
SODIUM HYDROXIDE

b)   Use the words below to answer the following questions.

nitrogen   chlorine   hydrogen   potassium

i)   What is produced at the anode during the electrolysis of brine?   ....

ii) What is produced at the cathode during the electrolysis of brine? ....

Q6   The diagram shows the **pH scale**.

1	2	3	4	5	6	7	8	9	10	11	12	13

↑ black coffee   ↑ magnesium hydroxide

a)   The pH values of black coffee and magnesium hydroxide are marked on the diagram.

i)   Is black coffee neutral, acidic or alkaline? ....

ii) Is magnesium hydroxide neutral, acidic or alkaline? ....

b)   What type of reaction would occur between black coffee and magnesium hydroxide?

....

c)   Indigestion is caused by too much acid in the stomach.
Explain why magnesium hydroxide would be useful in indigestion tablets.

....

d)   Does universal indicator show a **sudden** or **gradual** change in colour as pH changes?

....

Q7   Ammonia is produced by the **Haber process**.

a)   Nitrogen and hydrogen are used to make ammonia. State where they come from.

i) nitrogen ....

ii) hydrogen ....

b)   The cost of the raw materials is one factor that affects how much it costs to make ammonia.
Give **three other factors** that affect the cost.

....

....

Using the Sun's Energy

Q1 Tick to show whether the sentences below are **true** or **false**.

                                                                True   **False**

a) Wind turbines directly convert heat into electricity. ☐ ☐

b) Most of the Sun's energy that reaches the Earth is light and heat. ☐ ☐

c) The wind is a non-renewable source of energy. ☐ ☐

Q2 **Passive solar heating** can be used to heat things.
Circle the correct word in each of the following sentences.

a) Glass **lets through** / **absorbs** radiation from the Sun.

b) Objects get **cooler** / **warmer** when they absorb radiation.

c) Curved **rocks** / **mirrors** can focus light and heat from the Sun.

Q3 **Cells** and **batteries**, such as photocells, generate **direct current** (DC).

a) What is meant by **direct current**? Circle the correct words in the statement below.

Direct current means the current flows in **different directions** / **the same direction** all the time.

b) One of the statements below explains how the **surface area** of a photocell affects how much power it produces. Circle the correct statement from the list below.

A — The size of the surface area has no effect on the power output of a photocell.

B — The larger the surface area, the lower the power output of a photocell.

C — The larger the surface area, the greater the power output of a photocell.

Q4 **Wind turbines** can be used to generate electricity from moving **air**.

a) What is the original source of the wind energy that turns the turbine? Circle the correct answer.

What _causes_ the air to move?

turbine blades

electrical output

generator

Gravity   Heat from the Sun

b) Give one **environmental advantage** and one **environmental disadvantage** of wind turbines.

Advantage: ....

....

Disadvantage: ....

....

Top Tips: The Sun produces a huge amount of energy all the time so it makes sense to use some of it. Use your own energy to revise, and practise, and **read** the questions carefully in exams.

Using the Sun's Energy

Q5 Choose from the words below to complete the passage about **wind power**.

turbines	convection	kinetic	Sun	rises

When air is heated by the .... , hot air .... and cold air

whooshes in to take its place. This is a .... current, but we know it as wind.

Wind can be used to drive .... which change the ....

energy (movement) of the wind into electricity.

Q6 Tick the boxes to show whether these statements are **true** or **false**.

                                                                   True False

a) Photocells change energy from the Moon into electricity.

b) Passive solar heating is when energy from the Sun heats things directly.

c) Photocells work best on cloudy days.

d) Glass can block heat and light from the Sun.

Q7 Photocells are used to generate **electricity**.

a) Give **two advantages** of using photocells to generate electricity.

1. ....

2. ....

b) Give **one disadvantage** of using photocells to generate electricity.

....

Q8 **Passive solar heating** is used in many ways.

a) Greenhouses are used to keep plants warm while they grow.
Explain why greenhouses are made of **glass**.

....

....

b) Reggie wants to fry his eggs using a **solar oven**.
Complete the paths of the light rays on the diagram
to show how the solar oven heats the pan.

Curved mirror   Light ray

Light ray

Producing and Distributing Electricity

Q1   Complete the passage by choosing from the words given below.

National Grid	power stations	consumers	generated

Most electricity is produced by ....

The .... is the network of power lines that

covers the whole country. Power can be .... almost anywhere to

be supplied to .... (like homes and schools) almost anywhere.

Q2   In a large **power station**, there are several steps involved in making electricity.
Number the steps below in the right order from 1 to 5. 1 has been done for you.

☐	Hot steam makes a turbine spin.
☐	Electricity is produced by the spinning generator.
1	Fuel is used to produce heat.
☐	The spinning turbine makes the generator spin too.
☐	Water is heated to make steam.

Q3   Different power stations use different types of **fuel** to generate electricity.

a)   Write the five **fuels** given below in the correct columns of the table to match their **fuel type**.

plutonium

wood

straw

crude oil

coal

Fossil fuel	Nuclear fuel	Biomass

b)   Give **one other** example of each fuel type.

i) Fossil fuel   ....

ii) Nuclear fuel   ....

iii) Biomass   ....

Q4   Give one **advantage** and one **disadvantage** of using the following types of **fuel** in power stations.

a)   Fossil fuels: Advantage: ....

                Disadvantage: ....

b)   Biomass: Advantage: ....

                Disadvantage: ....

The Dynamo Effect

Q1   Adrian is using the equipment in the diagram below to show the **dynamo effect**.

Choose from the following words to complete the passage below.

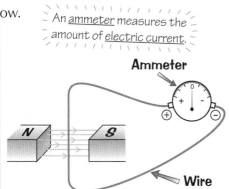

An *ammeter* measures the amount of *electric current*.

Ammeter

current	field	wire	alternating
As Adrian moves the .... near the magnet,			
it passes through a magnetic			
This produces a .... in the wire.			
By moving the wire in and out of the magnetic field Adrian			
produces an .... current in the wire.			

Wire

Q2   Look at the simple **generators** sketched below.

Coil spread over greater area

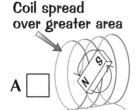

A ☐

Quicker rotation

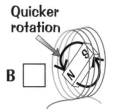

B ☐

Stronger magnet

C ☐

One of the generators labelled A - C will **not** produce a higher current than the generator in the box on the left. Tick the box next to that generator.

Q3   Moving a **magnet** inside a **coil** of wire can produce an image on a **display**.

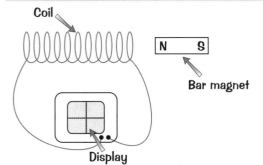

Coil

Bar magnet

Display

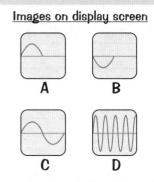

Images on display screen

A   B

C   D

When the magnet was **pushed inside** the coil, image **A** was produced on the display.

Draw lines to match the images to how they could have been produced:

| Image B |

| Pushing the magnet in and pulling it out again straight away. |

| Image C |

| Quickly moving the magnet in and out of the coil a few times. |

| Image D |

| By pulling the magnet out of the coil. |

Supplying Electricity Efficiently

Q1 **Number** these statements 1 to 5 to show the order of the steps that are needed to **send electricity** to Mrs Miggins' house so that she can boil the kettle. The last step has been done for you.

	An electrical current flows through **power cables** across the country.
5	Mrs Miggins **boils the kettle** for tea.
	Electricity comes from a **power station**.
	The voltage of the electricity is made **higher**.
	The voltage of the electricity is made **lower**.

Q2 The sentences below each contain **one** mistake.
Write out a correct version of each by changing the **highlighted** words.

a) The National Grid transmits energy at high voltage and **high** current.

....

b) Transformers **reduce** the voltage of electricity before it flows across the country.

....

c) Sending out electricity at a high **current** wastes less energy.

....

Q3 Use the **efficiency formula** to complete the table. The first one has been done for you.

Total Energy Input (J)	Useful Energy Output (J)	Efficiency
2000	1500	0.75
4000	2000	
4000	1000	

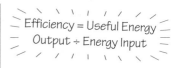

Efficiency = Useful Energy Output ÷ Energy Input

Q4 **One litre** of oil produces **6 MJ** of energy when it is burned.
A power station uses **40 litres of oil each second**. It **wastes 168 MJ** of energy each second.

a) How much energy is **input** each second into the power station from burning oil?

.... MJ

b) How much of this input energy is **useful**?

.... MJ

c) What is the **efficiency** of the power station?

....

Power

Q1 Tick to show whether the following statements are **true** or **false**.

	True	False
a) Power is measured in watts.	☐	☐
b) Voltage is measured in watts.	☐	☐
c) The cost of using an electric kettle depends only on its power rating.	☐	☐

Q2 The **current** an appliance uses depends on its **power** rating. Complete the table below to show the power rating of various appliances at mains voltage — **230 V**.

Appliance	Current (A)	Power (W)
Kettle	10	2300
Radio	0.1	
Laptop computer	0.35	
Lamp	0.17	

Power = voltage × current

Q3 Luigi cooks a pizza for his tea. It takes him **half an hour** to cook his pizza in a **2.3 kW** oven.

a) How much **energy** is used to cook the pizza? Circle the correct answer.

Energy = power × time

1.5 kWh   **2.3 kWh**   **1.15 kWh**

b) Luigi has to pay 12p per kWh. How much does it **cost** him to cook his pizza?

....

Cost = number of kWh × price per kWh

Q4 A tumble drier operating on a **230 V household supply** uses a current of **8 A**.

1 kW = 1000 W

a) Calculate the **power rating** of the tumble drier in kW.

....

.... kW

b) How much **energy** does the tumble drier use in 2 hours? Give your answer in kWh.

.... kWh

c) Electricity costs 11.5p per kWh. How much does it **cost** to use the tumble drier for 2 hours?

.... p

Power

Q5 Mr Havel recently received his **electricity bill**. Unfortunately, he tore off the bottom part.

Customer : Mr. V. Havel

Date	Meter Reading
June 11th	34259
September 10th	34783

Total Cost @ 9.7p per kWh

a) The bill uses units of **kilowatt-hours** (kWh). What is a kilowatt-hour?

....

....

b) How many **kWh** of energy did Mr Havel use in the three months from June to September?

Work out the difference between the meter readings.

.... kWh

c) Calculate the **total cost** of Mr. Havel's electricity bill.

.... p

Q6 Boris puts his **2 kW** electric heater on for 3 hours.

a) Calculate how many **kilowatt-hours** of electrical energy the heater uses.

.... kWh.

b) Boris's electricity costs 7p per kilowatt-hour. Work out the **cost** of the energy calculated in part **a)**.

.... p

c) Boris leaves a 60 W lamp on for 9 hours every day. Boris's wife uses an 8 kW shower for 15 mins every day.

Who uses the **most energy** per day? Calculate how much energy each person uses and compare your results.

Make sure the units are right before you do any calculations.

i) Boris uses:

....

.... kWh

ii) Boris's wife uses:

....

.... kWh

iii) Circle the name of the person who uses the most energy: **Boris / Boris's wife**.

Top Tips: Lots of maths on these pages, but practice makes perfect. One day you'll have your own electricity bills to sort out and then you'll be glad you learnt all this (and it could be on the exam).

The Greenhouse Effect

Q1 The diagram below shows how the **greenhouse effect** keeps the Earth warm. Use the descriptions **A** to **C** to label the diagram with the correct letters.

A
The Earth gives off some of the heat radiation.

B
Greenhouse gases absorb radiation from Earth, stopping it radiating back into space.

C
The Earth absorbs radiation from the Sun.

Q2 Tick the boxes next to the **three** greenhouse gases below.

nitrogen ☐   water vapour ☐   carbon dioxide ☐

oxygen ☐   methane ☐   helium ☐

Q3 Which of the statements below best describes the **greenhouse effect**? Circle the **one** correct statement.

A   Global warming is caused by humans releasing more greenhouse gases.

B   A process which keeps the Earth warm.

C   A chemical reaction in the atmosphere which releases heat.

D   The natural heating effect of the Sun.

Q4 Greenhouse gases can come from **natural** and **man-made** sources.

a) i) Give **one natural source** of carbon dioxide in the atmosphere.

....

ii) Give **two man-made sources** of carbon dioxide.

1. ....

2. ....

b)   List **one natural** and **one man-made** source of the greenhouse gas methane.

Natural: ....

Man-made: ....

Global Warming and Climate Change

Q1   Complete the passage by choosing from the words below.

carbon	greenhouse	temperatures	increased

Global .... have .... in
recent years. This is because the .... effect has been
upset by too much .... dioxide in the atmosphere.

Q2   Below are six statements about **global warming** and **climate change**.
Tick the boxes to show whether each statement is true or false.

True   **False**

a)   The temperature of the Earth is decreasing. ☐ ☐

b)   The amount of carbon dioxide in the atmosphere has been increasing. ☐ ☐

c)   Global warming is caused by climate change. ☐ ☐

d)   Humans are definitely not to blame for global warming. ☐ ☐

e)   Global warming can affect the weather. ☐ ☐

f)   It's easy to measure global warming. ☐ ☐

Q3   Climate change, like changes in temperatures, can be caused by
human activity and **natural** events like volcanoes.

a)   Deforestation is a human cause of climate change.

   i)   Does deforestation **increase** or **decrease** the amount of carbon dioxide in the atmosphere?

   ....

   ii)   Explain why deforestation changes the amount of carbon dioxide in the atmosphere.

   ....

   ....

b)   Describe the effect **ash** from a volcano could have on the Earth's temperature.

   ....

   ....

Top Tips: You need to know how global warming and climate change affect the Earth.
It's not just so you can pass exams — serious changes could happen in your lifetime.

Nuclear Radiation and Power

Q1 Tick the boxes to show which of these statements are **true** and which are **false**.

True False

a) Negative ions are formed when atoms lose electrons. ☐ ☐

b) The energy released from radioactive material is used to drive turbines. ☐ ☐

c) Nuclear power produces lots of greenhouse gases. ☐ ☐

d) Uranium is a non-renewable energy resource. ☐ ☐

e) Ionisation is harmful because it can damage living cells. ☐ ☐

Q2 **Radioactive waste** can be hard to **dispose** of.

a) Some radioactive waste can be recycled into useful material. What is this process called?

reprocessing   **renewing**

b) Describe **two** ways of disposing of radioactive waste.

1. ....

....

2. ....

....

Q3 Two scientists are working with samples of radioactive material.

a) One of the scientists is working **safely**, but the other scientist **is not**.
Describe **two** things that the careless scientist is doing wrong.

1. ....

2. ....

b) Where should radioactive samples be stored when they are not in use?

....

Uses of Nuclear Radiation

Q1   Radioactive materials give out **nuclear radiation**.

List the **three** types of nuclear radiation.

1. ....   2. ....   3. ....

Q2   Nuclear radiation is used in **hospitals**.

a)   Which type of nuclear radiation can be used to treat **cancer**? ....

b)   Which **two** types of nuclear radiation are used as **tracers** inside the body?

1. ....   2. ....

Q3   The following sentences explain how a **smoke detector** works, but they are in the wrong order. Put them in order by labelling them 1 to 4. 1 has been done for you.

| 1 | The radioactive source emits alpha radiation.

| | The alarm sounds.

| | A fire starts and gives off smoke.

| | Smoke particles absorb the alpha radiation.

Q4   Brian was investigating **three** radioactive sources — A, B and C.
Radiation from each source was aimed at sheets of **paper**, **aluminium** and an **unknown sheet**.
Counters were used to detect where radiation passed through the target sheets.

Results:
Source A — gives off gamma radiation, which was stopped by the unknown sheet.
Source B — the radiation was stopped by the paper.
Source C — the radiation was stopped by the aluminium.

a)   What type of radiation is given off by:

i)   Source B? ....

ii)   Source C? ....

b)   What material was the unknown sheet made from?

....

Uses of Nuclear Radiation

Q5 **Different types** of nuclear radiation are used for different things.

a) Draw a line to match the type of radiation with its use.
Draw a second line to match its use with an explanation of why it's used.

Alpha   Paper thickness control   Kills living cells.

Beta   Treating cancer   Can pass through paper.

Gamma   Smoke detectors   Stopped by smoke particles.

b) Give **one** other use for:

i) Gamma radiation ....

ii) Beta radiation ....

Q6 **Gamma radiation** can be used in the non-destructive testing of turbine blades in jet engines.

a) What does non-destructive testing mean?

....

....

b) The diagram to the right shows a jet turbine blade being tested for cracks using gamma radiation. The gamma detector measures how much gamma radiation gets through the metal blade.

gamma radiation source → gamma detector / jet turbine blade

How can you tell if the blade has a crack in it?
Circle the correct answer.

A — If no radiation gets through the blade there's a crack.

B — If a lot of radiation gets through the blade there's a crack.

Q7 The diagram on the right shows how **beta radiation** can be used to control paper thickness.

beta radiation source / PAPER / beta detector

Why is beta radiation used, rather than alpha or gamma?

Think about the penetrating power of the different types of radiation.

....

....

....

The Solar System and the Universe

Q1 This diagram shows the most important objects in the Solar System. It **isn't to scale**.

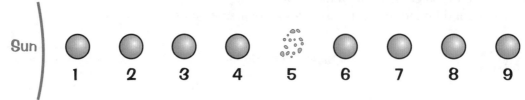

Sun) 1 2 3 4 5 6 7 8 9

In the table below, write the correct number under each name
to show its position in the Solar System. One has been done for you.

Body	Mars	Jupiter	Asteroids	Venus	Saturn	Neptune	Earth	Mercury	Uranus
Number						9			

Q2 The Universe contains **stars** and **planets**,
some of which can be seen from Earth.

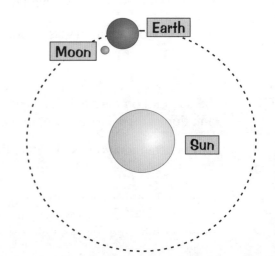

a) List **three** other things that the Universe contains.

1. ....

2. ....

3. ....

b) Why can we see stars from Earth even though they're far away?

....

Q3 Gravity causes the **Earth** to orbit the **Sun** as shown in the diagram.

a) Draw the orbit of the Moon on the diagram.

b) Explain how gravity makes **black holes** black.

....

....

....

....

Asteroids and Comets

Q1   Choose from the words in the box below to **complete** the passage.

extinct	climate	Sun	Earth

Asteroids orbit the .... Sometimes they leave their orbits and collide

with the .... When this happens it can cause ....

change and cause species to become ....

Q2   As well as planets, there are **asteroids** and **comets** in the Solar System.

a) The asteroids orbit in the **asteroid belt**. The asteroid belt is between which two planets?

.... and ....

b) What are asteroids made of?

....

c) Circle the correct word in each pair.

Comets are made of ice and **black holes** / **dust**.

The tail of a comet is a trail of **asteroids** / **debris**.

d) Where do comets come from?

....

Q3   Scientists think that a very large **asteroid** hit the Earth about 65 million years ago and caused the **extinction** of over half the species on Earth.

a) There is **evidence** to show that asteroids have collided with the Earth in the past.
Tick **two** boxes that describe this evidence.

☐ There are layers of unusual elements in rocks on Earth.

☐ There are volcanoes where the asteroids hit.

☐ Comets are made from asteroids that hit the Earth.

☐ There are sudden changes in the number of fossils in different layers of rock.

b) Other than extinction, give **two** problems that could be caused by asteroids hitting the Earth.

1. ....

2. ....

Asteroids and Comets

Q4   Draw a line to match up the word to the correct description of **where they come from**.

Asteroids

Comets

Left over from when the Solar System was made.

Come from objects orbiting the Sun a lot further away than the planets.

Q5   The diagram shows the orbit of a **comet** around the Sun.

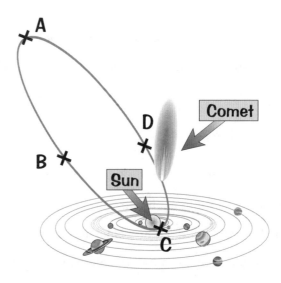

a)   What is the name of the **shape** of the comet's orbit?

....

b)   Write down the **letter** that shows at what point (**A** to **D**) the comet is travelling fastest and slowest.

i)   The comet is travelling fastest at point: ....

ii) The comet is travelling slowest at point: ....

c)   Explain your answer to part **b)**.

....

....

d)   What are comets made of?

....

Top Tips: Don't get asteroids and comets mixed up. Asteroids stay in the asteroid belt where they belong (well, they do most of the time), and comets have really long orbits that take them even further out than the furthest planets, and really close in to the Sun.

NEOs and the Moon

Q1 The following diagrams show how scientists think the **Moon** was formed.

Number the diagrams in the correct order from 1-4.

| Low density bits flew off and orbited the Earth. ☐ | The iron cores of the planets merged at very high temperatures. ☐ |

| A small planet collided with the Earth. ☐ | The bits eventually came together to form the Moon. ☐ |

Q2 Describe what is meant by a **light year**.

....

....

Q3 Some astronomers work on finding **Near Earth Objects** (**NEO**s).

a) Circle the correct word in each pair to complete the statement about NEOs.

NEOs are asteroids or **planets / comets** which might collide with the **Earth / Sun**.

b) What do astronomers use to keep an eye on NEOs?

....

c) Why do astronomers keep an eye on NEOs?
Circle the correct statement.

A — Because NEOs affect the Earth's gravity.

B — Because NEOs could collide with the Earth.

C — Because NEOs could leave the Solar System.

d) Give **two** reasons why it is difficult to keep an eye on NEOs.

1. ....

2. ....

Understanding the Universe

Q1 **Radiation** coming from space can tell astronomers a lot about the **Solar System** and the **Universe**.

The diagram below shows what the Solar System looks like.

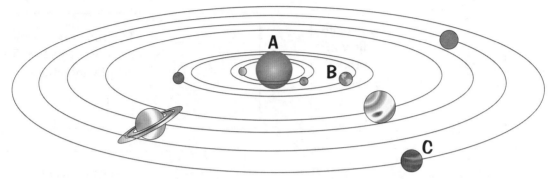

Is there anywhere in the Solar System where there's **no microwave radiation**?
Circle the correct answer.

Point A   Point B   Point C   There's microwave radiation everywhere.

Q2 Draw lines to match up the **beginning and end** of each of the sentences below.

Radio signals take...

...don't need food, water or oxygen.

Manned spacecraft...

...a long time to travel through the Solar System.

Unmanned probes...

...need to take food, water and oxygen.

Q3 The **Big Bang** theory is one theory that tries to explain how the Universe started.

a) Complete this passage using the words listed below.

explosion	small	expand
Scientists believe that everything in the Universe was packed into a very .... space. Then there was a huge .... and the Universe started to		

b) What is the Universe doing now? Circle the correct answer.

it's contracting   it's still expanding   it's neither contracting
(shrinking)   nor expanding

Understanding the Universe

Q4 We can send **manned** or **unmanned** space craft to explore space.

a) Name **three** things that manned spacecraft need that unmanned probes do not.

1. ....

2. ....

3. ....

b) One other advantage of using unmanned probes rather than manned spacecraft is given below. Circle the correct answer from the statements below.

A — They can think for themselves.

B — They can travel faster than humans.

C — They can cope with conditions that would be fatal to humans.

Q5 Manned spacecraft and unmanned probes can collect **information** from places in the Solar System.

a) How could information be sent back to Earth from the **Moon** (close to Earth)?

....

b) How could information be sent back to Earth from **Saturn** (very far from Earth)?

....

Q6 Here are some statements about the expansion of the Universe. Tick the boxes to show whether each statement is **true** or **false**.

	True	False
a) Most galaxies are moving **away** from the Earth.	☐	☐
b) The further away a galaxy is the **slower** it is moving.	☐	☐
c) The Universe is **contracting**.	☐	☐
d) The Universe started from a **single** point.	☐	☐
e) Microwave radiation comes from **all parts of** the Universe.	☐	☐

Top Tips: The Big Bang — everything was squished up in a tiny space... then BANG, the Universe starts expanding. Make sure you know a bit about microwave radiation too.

The Life Cycle of Stars

Q1   Stars take a long time to **form**.

a)   What are stars made from?

....

b)   What force causes this material to come together? ....

Q2   Complete the passage below using the words provided.

neutron	supernova	supergiants	white	nebula	red	black

When stars get old they swell and become .... giants. Small stars

eject their outer layer as a planetary .... and their core becomes a

.... dwarf. Big stars become red ....

which explode in a .... The star then becomes a

.... star or a .... hole.

Due to printing restrictions, red giants are unavailable.

Q3   The diagram below shows the final stages in the life of a **small star** like the Sun.

star   A   B   and   C

a)   Write down the name of each of the following:

i) A ....

ii) B ....

iii) C ....

b)   Why does the star change colour when it changes into **A**?

....

c)   Describe what happens to the star from stage **A** to stage **C**.

....

....

....

Galileo and Copernicus

Q1 Circle the correct word in the following sentences.

a) The planets all orbit the Earth in the **Ptolemaic** / **Copernican** model.

b) **Ptolemy** / **Copernicus** said the Sun was at the centre of the Universe.

c) The Copernican model says that the planets all orbit the **Sun** / **Moon**.

d) The orbits of the planets in the Copernican model are all perfect **circles** / **ellipses**.

e) Evidence for the Copernican model was found by **Ptolemy** / **Galileo**.

f) The Ptolemaic model is also a **heliocentric** / **geocentric** model.

An egocentric model.

Q2 Galileo made some observations of **Jupiter** and **Venus** that helped to provide evidence for the **Copernican** model of the Solar System.

a) What technological advance helped Galileo? Circle the correct answer.

Unmanned probes   Telescopes   Telephones

b) Choose the **two** correct statements below to describe what Galileo saw when looking at Jupiter and Venus.

☐ The moons of Jupiter

☐ The moons of Venus

☐ The phases of Jupiter

☐ The phases of Venus

c) Complete the passage below using words from the list.

Ptolemaic	Earth	Jupiter	Venus	small	big

Galileo saw moons orbiting .... This showed not everything was in orbit

around the .... — so the .... model was wrong.

Galileo also noticed that .... has phases (like the Moon). If the Ptolemaic

model was right then the changes would be .... But if a Copernican

model was right, the changes would be .... — this is what Galileo saw.

Top Tips: New technology changed our idea of how the Solar System worked. Make sure that you know what Copernicus' great idea was, and what Galileo saw that showed it might be right.

Mixed Questions — Module P2

Q1 Tick the boxes to show which of these statements are **true** and which are **false**.

True False

a) The Moon was formed after another planet collided with the Earth. ☐ ☐

b) Geocentric means the Sun is at the centre of the Solar System. ☐ ☐

c) Unmanned probes carry people into space. ☐ ☐

d) Microwave radiation is everywhere in the Universe. ☐ ☐

e) Small stars eventually become black holes. ☐ ☐

f) Comets have small, circular orbits around the Sun. ☐ ☐

Q2 Electricity is generated in **power stations** and reaches our homes by a network of **power cables**.

a) In a gas-fired power station, natural **gas** is burned to produce heat energy.

 i) Circle the correct word in each pair to complete the sentences below.

  The heat is used to make **oil** / **steam** which turns a **turbine** / **magnet**.

  This then turns a generator which converts **kinetic** / **nuclear** energy into electrical energy.

 ii) Name **two** other types of fuel that can be used in a power station to produce heat.

  .... and ....

b) Electricity can also be generated from photocells.

 i) Choose the **one** correct statement to explain why photocells aren't very reliable in the UK.

  A — Because it's too cold in the UK.

  B — Because there's not enough sunny days in the UK.

  C — Because most houses in the UK have the wrong type of roofs.

 ii) Draw a line to match the power source to the type of current it produces.

  | Generator in a power station | | Alternating current (AC) |
  | Photocell | | Direct current (DC) |

c) i) Explain why electricity is sent out through power cables at very high voltages.

  ....

  ....

 ii) What device is used to convert this high voltage into a safer, lower voltage for use in a house?

  ....

Module P2 — Living for the Future

Mixed Questions — Module P2

Q3 The table gives information about three different **radioactive materials**.

a) Which of these materials would you use in:

i) a smoke detector?

....

ii) non-destructive testing?

....

Material	Type of Radiation
krypton-85	beta
selenium-75	gamma
americium-241	alpha

iii) a machine controlling paper thickness? ....

b) List **two** things that workers should do in order to work safely with these radioactive materials.

1. ....

2. ....

c) Fill in the **blanks** in each statement about radioactive materials.

i) .... is used as a fuel in nuclear power stations.

ii) .... is a waste product that can be used to make nuclear weapons.

iii) Radioactive waste is often sealed into .... blocks and buried deep underground.

Q4 Our **model** of the Solar System and what's in it has **changed** over time.

a) i) Name the furthest planet in the Solar System from the Sun.

....

ii) Give **two** reasons why it would be **difficult** to send a **manned** spacecraft to this planet.

1. ....

2. ....

b) Put the statements below in order from 1- 4 to show how models of the Solar System have changed over time. The first one has been done for you.

☐ Galileo found **evidence** that supported Copernicus.

☐ **Copernicus** said that everything orbited the Sun.

[1] The **Ptolemaic** model said that everything orbited the Earth.

☐ **Galileo** used a telescope to look at Jupiter and Venus.

Mixed Questions — Module P2

Q5 Jemima is using an **electric sander** which uses a current of **2 A**.

a) The electricity supply in Jemima's house is at 230 V. Calculate the **power** of the sander:

   i) in watts ....

   ii) in kW ....

Power = voltage × current

b) Jemima has the sander on for **0.5 hours**. How much energy does she use in kWh?

....

....

Units of energy = power × time

c) Jemima's electricity supplier charges **15p per kWh**.
How much does it **cost** to use the sander for 0.5 hours?

....

d) The power station that supplies Jemima's electricity produces **380 J** of **useful** energy for every **1000 J** of energy **input**. What is its efficiency?

....

$$Efficiency = \frac{useful\ energy\ output}{total\ energy\ input}$$

Q6 **Planets**, **moons**, **asteroids**, **comets** and the **Sun** are all found in the Solar System.

a) The Sun is a **small star**.

   i) Will the Sun ever become a **black hole**? ....

   ii) Explain your answer to part **i)** by circling the correct statement below.

   | It's too old | It's close enough to the Earth | It's too small |

b) Fill in the blanks in the sentences using the words listed below them.

   i) The Moon was made after a .... collided with the Earth.
      moon   planet   asteroid

   ii) The .... cores merged to form the Earth's core.
      iron   helium   carbon

   iii) Less .... material was ejected as dust and rock.
      icy   dusty   dense

c) Tick the boxes to show which of these statements are **true** and which are **false**.

	True	False
i) **Unusual elements** in rocks may have been brought to Earth by asteroids.	☐	☐
ii) Asteroids are usually found orbiting the Sun between **Mercury** and **Venus**.	☐	☐
iii) Comets **speed up** as they get closer to the Sun.	☐	☐
iv) Dust from asteroid impacts has caused **climate change** in the past.	☐	☐